THE INTERNATIONAL ENCYCLOPEDIA OF PHYSICAL CHEMISTRY AND CHEMICAL PHYSICS

Topic 17. MACROMOLECULES

EDITOR: C. E. H. BAWN

Volume 1

THE KINETICS OF FREE RADICAL POLYMERIZATION

BY

A. M. NORTH

THE INTERNATIONAL ENCYCLOPEDIA
OF PHYSICAL CHEMISTRY AND CHEMICAL PHYSICS

THE INTERNATIONAL ENCYCLOPEDIA
OF PHYSICAL CHEMISTRY AND CHEMICAL PHYSICS

Editors-in-Chief

E. A. GUGGENHEIM
READING

J. E. MAYER
LA JOLLA

F. C. TOMPKINS
LONDON

Chairman of the Editorial Advisory Group

ROBERT MAXWELL
PUBLISHER AT PERGAMON PRESS

List of Topics and Editors

1. Mathematical Techniques — H. JONES, *London*
2. Classical and Quantum Mechanics — R. MCWEENY, *Keele*
3. Electronic Structure of Atoms — C. A. HUTCHISON, JR., *Chicago*
4. Molecular Binding — J. W. LINNETT, *Cambridge*
5. Molecular Properties
    (*a*) Electronic — J. W. LINNETT, *Cambridge*
    (*b*) Non-electronic — N. SHEPPARD, *East Anglia*
6. Kinetic Theory of Gases — E. A. GUGGENHEIM, *Reading*
7. Classical Thermodynamics — D. H. EVERETT, *Bristol*
8. Statistical Mechanics — J. E. MAYER, *La Jolla*
9. Transport Phenomena — J. C. MCCOUBREY, *Birmingham*
10. The Fluid State — J. S. ROWLINSON, *London*
11. The Ideal Crystalline State — M. BLACKMAN, *London*
12. Imperfections in Solids — Editor to be appointed
13. Mixtures, Solutions, Chemical and Phase Equilibria — M. L. MCGLASHAN, *Exeter*
14. Properties of Interfaces — D. H. EVERETT, *Bristol*
15. Equilibrium Properties of Electrolyte Solutions — R. A. ROBINSON, *Washington, D.C.*
16. Transport Properties of Electrolytes — R. H. STOKES, *Armidale*
17. Macromolecules — C. E. H. BAWN, *Liverpool*
18. Dielectric and Magnetic Properties — J. W. STOUT, *Chicago*
19. Gas Kinetics — A. F. TROTMAN-DICKENSON, *Aberystwyth*
20. Solution Kinetics — R. M. NOYES, *Eugene*
21. Solid and Surface Kinetics — F. C. TOMPKINS, *London*
22. Radiation Chemistry — R. S. LIVINGSTON, *Minneapolis*

THE KINETICS OF
FREE RADICAL
POLYMERIZATION

BY

ALASTAIR M. NORTH

DEPARTMENT OF INORGANIC, PHYSICAL AND
INDUSTRIAL CHEMISTRY,
THE UNIVERSITY OF LIVERPOOL,
LIVERPOOL, ENGLAND

PERGAMON PRESS

OXFORD . LONDON . EDINBURGH . NEW YORK
TORONTO . PARIS . BRAUNSCHWEIG

Pergamon Press Ltd., Headington Hill Hall, Oxford
4 & 5 Fitzroy Square, London W.1
Pergamon Press (Scotland) Ltd., 2 & 3 Teviot Place, Edinburgh 1
Pergamon Press Inc., 44–01 21st Street, Long Island City, New York 11101
Pergamon of Canada, Ltd., 6 Adelaide Street East, Toronto, Canada
Pergamon Press S.A.R.L., 24 rue des Écoles, Paris 5ᵉ
Vieweg & Sohn GmbH, Burgplatz 1, Braunschweig

First edition 1966

Library of Congress Catalog Card No. 66–21138

PRINTED IN GREAT BRITAIN AT THE PITMAN PRESS, BATH
2821/66

CONTENTS

CHAPTER 1

INTRODUCTION

SEVERAL decades have passed since the realization that certain vinyl and related compounds could be converted to high polymers by the action of labile molecules known to produce free radicals. These radical-produced polymerization processes were very rapidly shown to be chain reactions, the general kinetics of which showed all the characteristic features of consecutive initiation, propagation and termination steps. Because a general understanding of the kinetics and mechanism of free radical polymerization has existed for several years, recent research and interest in this field has been rather differently oriented in comparison with work on other polymerization processes. Indeed the problems of current interest in free radical polymerization are of a rather detailed or specific nature.

Despite the detailed nature of present studies, it is not a valid criticism that these efforts are merely "filling-in" unimportant gaps in existing knowledge. Many of the detailed problems, such as the applicability of stationary-state approximations or the role of diffusion in fast radical reactions, have an importance extending well beyond the field of polymer processes.

This series of monographs is designed to function both as an introduction to a specific field and as a reflection of current interest in the field. For this reason the two chapters on General Kinetics and Determination of Individual Rate Constants form a general introduction to the standard kinetic analyses of free radical polymerization. The first sections of the chapters dealing with individual reactions serve the same purpose. However, later sections deal in some detail with certain of the topics that are at present of interest to research workers in free radical polymerization. It is thereby hoped to present a picture of the field which is instructive and illustrative, without becoming a detailed compendium of every published paper.

CHAPTER 2

GENERAL KINETICS

A KINETIC study of free radical polymerization reactions may be carried out using either of the two principal theories of rate processes. Although the application of such theories to chemical kinetics is dealt with in another volume of this series, it is relevant to summarize the important points of these theories before progressing to their significance in polymerization kinetics.

The Collision Theory

The basis of a collision theory of chemical reactions is a computation of the frequency of collision between reactant species, together with the fraction of these collisions which result in chemical reaction.

The molecular configuration of both reactants and products must represent energy minima. Consequently at some point during the reaction the nuclei of the atoms involved possess a configuration of energy higher than both of these minima. There will, in fact, be an energy maximum, and the difference between this maximum and the energy of the reactants provides an energy barrier to reaction, called the activation energy. Consequently only those collisions between reactants which possess either kinetic or electronic excitation energy in excess of this activation energy can possibly lead to chemical reaction. The Maxwell–Boltzman distribution of molecular energies allows computation of the fraction of molecules in any system which contain energy, distributed between n square terms, greater than an amount ε,

$$f = \exp\left(-\frac{\varepsilon}{kT}\right)\left[\frac{1}{(\frac{1}{2}n-1)!}\left(\frac{\varepsilon}{kT}\right)^{1/2n-1} + \frac{1}{(\frac{1}{2}n-2)!}\left(\frac{\varepsilon}{kT}\right)^{1/2n-2} + \ldots + 1\right] \quad (2.1)$$

which for energy distributed over two square terms reduces to

$$\exp\left(-\frac{\varepsilon}{kT}\right)$$

Unfortunately, in the case of reactions between molecules other than simple spherical atoms energy transfer conditions over and above possession of the requisite amount of kinetic energy may have to be satisfied. When the reactive centre of a molecule is localized on the molecule, only those collisions involving contact at the locus of reactivity will result in reaction. These conditions, and the allowance for distribution of energy over more than two square terms, are taken into account by an empirical steric or probability factor p. Consequently, the frequency of chemical reaction is

$$k = p\mathscr{Z} \exp\left(-\frac{\varepsilon}{kT}\right) \tag{2.2}$$

where $\mathscr{Z}$ is the frequency of collision between reactant molecules.

The collision frequency in gases of spherical molecules with no interaction is

$$\mathscr{Z} = 2\left(\frac{\pi RT}{M}\right)^{1/2} \sigma^2 n^2 \tag{2.3}$$

where M is the molecular weight and σ the diameter of the molecule, and n is the number of molecules per cm^3. For collision between unlike molecules

$$\mathscr{Z}_{AB} = 2(2\pi RT[M_A^{-1} + M_B^{-1}])^{1/2} \sigma_{AB}^2 n_A n_B \tag{2.4}$$

where σ_{AB} is the mean molecular diameter. A simple treatment of non-spherical molecules with finite interactions is not possible, although a simple empirical allowance for interactions can be made by replacing the molecular diameter by an arbitrary collision radius, generally larger than the mean diameter. Then the rate constant for bimolecular reactions in the gas phase is

$$k = 2p(2\pi RT[M_A^{-1} + M_B^{-1}])^{1/2}\sigma_{AB}^2 \exp\left(-\frac{\varepsilon}{kT}\right) \text{ cm}^3 \text{ molecules}^{-1} \text{ s}^{-1} \tag{2.5}$$

$$= \frac{2p}{10^3} (2\pi RT[M_A^{-1} + M_B^{-1}])^{1/2}\sigma_{AB}^2 N \exp\left(-\frac{E}{RT}\right) \text{ l mole}^{-1} \text{ s}^{-1} \tag{2.6}$$

Exact calculation of values for p and E is not possible, so that for most reactions theoretical calculations of the values for rate constants cannot be carried out.

Collision Frequency in Condensed Phases

Since many chemical reactions, and certainly most polymerization reactions, take place in the liquid phase, it is necessary to extend the collision theory to cover liquid and solid phases. While the fraction of collisions which involve molecules with the correct steric and energy requirements can still be expressed in the form

$$f = p \exp\left(-\frac{E}{RT}\right),$$

it is necessary to reinvestigate the frequency of collisions in a condensed system.

In either a solid or liquid a particular molecule may be considered as vibrating on a site on a regular lattice which may represent long or short range order in the system. The molecule may also be capable of undergoing jump diffusive displacements onto neighbouring lattice sites, thereby undergoing an irregular diffusive translation. In general the frequency of diffusive jumps will be very much less than the vibration frequency on the lattice site. Consequently any molecule may undergo many vibrational collisions with neighbouring molecules before undergoing translational diffusion into a region of different neighbours.

When two reactant molecules diffuse into nearest neighbour positions, they may undergo many collisions before separation. Such a prolonged series of collisions is often referred to as an "encounter", and in the case of very reactive molecules, each encounter will lead to chemical reaction.

The significance of any bimolecular rate constant for reaction in a condensed phase can be illustrated using the following simplified scheme.

$$A + B \underset{k_2}{\overset{k_1}{\rightleftharpoons}} A{:}B$$

$$A{:}B \xrightarrow{k_3} \text{Products} \tag{2.7}$$

where A and B represent reactant molecules in the condensed phase which are not nearest neighbours, and A:B represents the "encounter" when the reactants are nearest neighbours undergoing repeated collisions. In general the rate of formation of A:B will equal the rate of disappearance of such collision pairs, so that

$$\frac{d[\text{Products}]}{dt} = \frac{k_1 k_3}{k_2 + k_3}[A][B] \tag{2.8}$$

It is possible to evaluate two extreme cases. For very rapid translational diffusion of reactants and slow chemical reaction, $k_2 \gg k_3$ and the overall rate constant is given by

$$k = \frac{k_1 k_3}{k_2} = K_{AB} k_3 \qquad (2.9)$$

k_3 may be found from the number of collisions between species A and B vibrating on neighbouring lattice sites with a relative frequency, ν, and is $k_3 = p\nu \exp(-E/RT)$. $K_{AB} = k_1/k_2$ represents the equilibrium constant for the formation of "encounter-pairs" of reactant molecules.

There are several possible ways of calculating K_{AB}. For spherical reactants with no long-range interactions this is just related to the probability that one reactant molecule, which can exist with equal probability anywhere in space, finds itself in the nearest neighbour shell of another reactant. This probability can easily be calculated from the volume of the nearest neighbour shell, and yields

$$K_{AB} = 4\pi \overline{r}_{AB}^{2} \, \delta r \qquad (2.10)$$

where $\overline{r}_{AB}$ is the average separation of the centres of the two molecules in the "encounter-pair", and δr is the thickness of the nearest neighbour shell.

Benson[1] has derived a more elaborate evaluation of K_{AB} from a consideration of the lifetime of the "encounter-pair". This can be calculated from random-walk theory as

$$t_{AB} = \frac{2\overline{r}_{AB}^{2}}{6 D_{AB}} \exp(-\omega_{ABS}/kT) \qquad (2.11)$$

where $D_{AB} = D_A + D_B$ represents the diffusion constant of A relative to B, and ω_{ABS} is the energy of separation of A and B in the solvent S.

The encounter frequency of A and B is

$$Z_{AB} = 3x\gamma \overline{r}_{AB} D_{AB} \qquad (2.12)$$

where x is the coordination number and γ is the packing factor of the liquid lattice.

Then the equilibrium concentration of "encounter-pairs" for negligible chemical reaction is

$$N_{AB} = N_A N_B Z'_{AB} t_{AB} \qquad (2.13)$$

so that

$$K_{AB} = \gamma x \overline{r}_{AB}^{3} \exp(-\omega_{ABS}/kT) \text{ cm}^3 \text{ molecules}^{-1} \qquad (2.14)$$

The overall bimolecular reaction rate constant for reactants not exerting long-range forces is then

$$k = \frac{\gamma N}{10^3} \times \overline{r_{AB}}^3 \, p\nu \exp\left\{ -\frac{(E_A + \omega_{ABS})}{RT} \right\} \text{l mole}^{-1}\,\text{s}^{-1} \qquad (2.15)$$

It is important to note that both the pre-exponential and the exponential terms contain factors due to the equilibrium constant for reactant pair formation, a fact often ignored when theoretical conclusions are drawn from these parameters.

In the extreme case of very slow translational diffusion or for very rapid chemical reactions, $k_2 \ll k_3$ and the overall rate constant is given by

$$k = k_1 \qquad (2.16)$$

The simplest derivation of k_1 is obtained by considering the rate of diffusion of spherical particles, A, into a spherical infinite sink of radius $\overline{r_{AB}}$ which is centred on a particle, B.

$$k_1 = \frac{4\pi N}{10^3} \, \overline{r_{AB}} D_{AB} \text{ l mole}^{-1}\,\text{s}^{-1} \qquad (2.17)$$

Since this rate constant is independent of the chemical nature of the reactants, under this extreme condition the reaction is referred to as being "diffusion-controlled".

On the basis of a similar treatment to that outlined above Rabinowitch[2] has derived for the overall rate constant for reaction in a liquid,

$$k = \frac{x\nu \exp\left(-E_A/RT\right)}{N_0\{1 + \frac{1}{2}[\overline{r_{AB}}^2 \gamma'\nu \exp\left(-E_A/RT\right)/D_{AB}]\}} \text{ cm}^3\,\text{mole}^{-1}\,\text{s}^{-1} \qquad (2.18)$$

where x is the coordination number of the lattice, N_0 is the number of lattice points in unit volume, $\overline{r_{AB}}$ is the shortest distance between lattice points and γ' is a constant depending upon the probability that a diffusive jump will alter the coordination number, x.

It is worthy of note that all these expressions assume that the diffusive jump frequency of molecule A into the proximity of molecule B is the same as the jump frequency in the opposite direction; that is, the direction of jump diffusion is random. This may not be the case when reactants exerting long range coulombic forces are under consideration.

In the case of macromolecular reactions the diffusive processes may be of a complex nature, and may also involve quite a large "diffusion activation energy" so that it is always necessary to appreciate the diffusive contributions to any bimolecular rate constant involving macromolecules.

Transition State Theory

In any atomic or molecular process requiring activation energy, the atoms involved pass through a configuration intermediate between that of reactants and that of the products, which configuration represents a potential energy maximum. This configuration is then treated as a loose molecular complex with a finite concentration, being in equilibrium with reactants and products to which it may revert. This complex has one conventional degree of freedom less than the reactants, which degree of freedom is replaced by a translational degree of freedom along a reaction coordinate

$$A + B \underset{}{\overset{k_1}{\rightleftharpoons}} X \xrightarrow{k_3} \text{Products}$$

Since k_3 is assumed to be much less than k_2, the pre-equilibrium is considered to be unperturbed by the chemical step.

$$\frac{d[\text{Products}]}{dt} = k_3 K_X [A][B] \tag{2.19}$$

where K_X is the equilibrium constant for the interchange,

$$A + B \rightleftharpoons X$$

Now by the use of statistical mechanics it can be shown that

$$K_X = \frac{Q'_X}{Q_A Q_B} \exp(-E_0/RT) \tag{2.20}$$

where Q'_X, Q_A, Q_B are the complete partition functions of species X, A, B respectively, and E_0 is the difference in the zero point energies of the two states. Factorizing out the partition function for one translational degree of freedom along the reaction coordinate

$$Q'_X = Q_X \left(\frac{2\pi m_X kT}{h^2} \right)^{1/2} \delta \tag{2.21}$$

where δ is an arbitrary distance along the reaction coordinate within which the transition complex may be assumed to have a definite existence, and m_X is the mass of the complex, X. Furthermore, the constant k_3 which has the dimensions of a frequency is given by

$$k_3 = \left(\frac{kT}{2\pi m_X} \right)^{1/2} \frac{1}{\delta} \tag{2.22}$$

and the overall rate constant for the reaction is thus

$$k = \frac{Q_X}{Q_A Q_B} \frac{kT}{h} \exp\left(-E_0/RT\right) \tag{2.23}$$

The rate constant can be expressed in terms of the thermodynamic functions of the species involved.

For the equilibrium between the reactants and the activated complex,

$$K_X = \exp\left(-\Delta H^*/RT\right) \exp\left(\Delta S^*/R\right) \tag{2.24}$$

where ΔH^* and ΔS^* represent the enthalpy and entropy differences respectively between the reactants and the transition complex.

Choosing a value for the arbitrary parameter δ

$$\delta = h/(2\pi m_X kT)^{1/2} \tag{2.25}$$

$$K_X = \frac{Q_X}{Q_A Q_B} \exp\left(-E_0/RT\right) \tag{2.26}$$

and thus the overall rate constant can also be expressed as

$$k = \frac{kT}{h} \exp\left(\Delta S^*/R\right) \exp\left(-\Delta H^*/RT\right) \tag{2.27}$$

As a good approximation $\Delta H^* = \Delta E^*$ when $\Delta H^* \gg RT$, and

$$k = \frac{kT}{h} \exp\left(\Delta S^*/R\right) \exp\left(-\Delta E^*/RT\right) \tag{2.28}$$

To take into account the fact that the reacting activated complex may revert to reactants after having passed the transition state of maximum energy, it is usual to introduce a "transmission coefficient" $\mathscr{K}$ of value close to unity,

$$k = \mathscr{K} \frac{kT}{h} \exp\left(\Delta S^*/R\right) \exp\left(-\Delta E^*/RT\right) \tag{2.29}$$

Transition State Model in Condensed Phases

Whatever the environment, the nth order rate constant is given by

$$k = k_3 K_X \frac{f_A f_B \cdots}{f_X} \tag{2.30}$$

where K_X is again the equilibrium constant for the formation of the transition state complex and $f_A, f_B, \ldots, f_X$ are the activity coefficients of the various reactants and the transition complex respectively.

It is of interest to compare the values predicted for k in gas phase and solution reactions.[1]

For dilute ideal solutions the activity coefficients may be approximated by unity when

$$\alpha_n = k_s/k_g = \frac{k_{3s}K_{Xs}}{k_{3g}K_{Xg}} \qquad (2.31)$$

where the subscripts s, g, refer to the solution and gaseous states respectively. k_3, being a vibration frequency, will be little affected by environment, when

$$\alpha_n = \frac{C_{Xs}C_{Ag}C_{Bg}}{C_{Xg}C_{As}C_{Bs}} \qquad (2.32)$$

all terms in C being equilibrium concentrations.

On replacing concentrations by the corresponding vapour pressure, and applying the Clausius–Clapeyron equation,

$$\alpha_n = \left(\frac{V_s^0}{RT}\right)^{n-1} \exp\left(\frac{-\Delta S_A^0 - \Delta S_B^0 - \ldots + \Delta S_X^0}{R}\right)$$
$$\exp\left(\frac{\Delta H_A^0 + \Delta H_B^0 + \ldots - \Delta H_X^0}{RT}\right) \qquad (2.33)$$

where V_s^0 is the molar volume of solvent, ΔS^0 and ΔH^0 are respectively the standard entropy and standard enthalpy of the relevant species.

To obtain a numerical value of the ratio α_n, it is possible to make use of the free volume theory of liquids when

$$\alpha_n = \frac{(V_s^0)^{n-1}V_{fX}^0}{V_{fA}^0 V_{fB}^0 \ldots} \exp\left(\frac{\partial \Delta H_v^0}{RT}\right) \qquad (2.34)$$

where V_{fi}^0 is the free volume of component, i, at its boiling point, and $\partial \Delta H_v^0$ is the difference in the heats of vaporization of the transition state complex, X, and the reactants.

For most liquids

$$\partial \Delta H_v^0 \sim -(n-1)RT, \quad V_s^0/V_{fi}^0 \sim 100, \quad V_{fX}^0/V_s^0 \sim \frac{n}{100} \qquad (2.35)$$

so that

$$\alpha_n \sim \frac{10^{2n-2}}{ne^{n-1}} \qquad (2.36)$$

Then the transition state theory predicts that the rate of a unimolecular reaction is the same in the gaseous phase as in solution, but that the ratio of rates is about 18 for bimolecular reactions and 450 for termolecular reactions, the solution rates being greater. This somewhat oversimplified example does not apply to reactions between charged species, the rates of which will be affected by the dielectric constant of the medium.

Simple Chain Reactions

A chain reaction is a series of consecutive reactions in which an activated species converts reactants to products, another activated molecule being formed in the process. In this way one initial activated molecule may be responsible for the conversion of many molecules of reactants. The commonest chain reactions are those involving free radicals as the reactive species, although chain reactions involving cations and anions are also well known.

There are three important steps in any chain reaction. The first is the initiation reaction by which the activated species are introduced into the reaction system. The second step, or series of steps is the propagation reaction, or reactions, by which reactants are converted to products with continuous regeneration of the activated species. The third step is the termination reaction by which the active chain carriers are removed from the system. The distinguishing feature of a chain reaction is the kinetic chain length, which is the number of molecules of reactant consumed per molecule of activated species formed in the initiation reaction.

Free radical polymerization exhibits the characteristic features of a chain reaction in that the overall reaction can be represented by a series of initiation, propagation and termination steps.

Initiation: $\text{Cat} \cdot \rightarrow \text{R}' \cdot$ Rate, R_i

$\text{R}' \cdot + \text{M} \rightarrow \text{R}_1$

Propagation: $R_n \cdot + \text{M} \rightarrow R_{n+1}$ Rate constant k_p

Termination: $R_m \cdot + R_s \cdot \rightarrow$ Inactive Polymer Rate constant k_t
where $\text{R}' \cdot$ represents a free radical formed from the catalyst, M is a monomer molecule, and $\text{R}_n \cdot$ represents a free radical containing n monomer units.

The propagation step differs from that of many other chain reactions in that the products are not formed directly in this step, and the radical formed differs always from the reacting radical in being attached to a polymer chain containing one more monomer unit. When the number of monomer units in the chain is very large, it might be expected that the addition of a further unit would not alter the chemical properties of the free radical to any noticeable extent. Under these circumstances the approximation might be made that the reactivity of the free radical is independent of its chain length and only one type of free radical is involved in the propagation of free radical polymerization. In this way the kinetic treatment of such a chain reaction may be greatly simplified.

An assumption which is applicable to many radical chain reactions and which allows further simplification of the kinetic treatment is the Bodenstein stationary state approximation. Owing to the high reactivity of free radicals, they very rapidly undergo a mutual termination reaction and are removed from the reaction system. If the initiation reaction is slow, an equilibrium situation is attained whereby the rate of formation of radicals is exactly balanced by their rate of disappearance. Under these circumstances an equilibrium concentration of free radicals will exist for any initiator concentration. As long as the initiator concentration is essentially unchanged, the equilibrium concentration of free radicals can be assumed to be constant. In any kinetic treatment of a radical chain reaction, it is possible to equate the rates of appearance and disappearance of free radicals so long as changes in the concentrations of initiating or terminating species take place over times that are very large compared with the times required to attain an equilibrium concentration of free radicals.

Simple Kinetics of Free Radical Polymerization

The kinetic features of interest in a free radical polymerization are the rate of polymerization, the kinetic chain length, the degree of polymerization, that is, the number of monomer units incorporated in each polymer molecule and the distribution of molecular weights which may characterize the resulting polymer. A simple kinetic treatment is one which will derive expressions relating these features to the variables of the reaction system such as reactant concentrations and the rate constants of the individual reactions, and at the same time make use of the two simplifying assumptions as to radical reactivity and concentration. Obviously such a simplified kinetic analysis can then only be applied to experimental conditions involving radicals with a high degree of polymerization, and involving times much greater than those required for the formation of a stationary state concentration of free radicals.

For long chains, monomer is consumed principally in the propagation reaction, when the rate of polymerization may be defined as

$$R_p = - \, \mathrm{d[M]}/\mathrm{d}t = k_p[\mathrm{M}][\mathrm{R} \cdot] \tag{2.37}$$

where $[\mathrm{R} \cdot]$ represents the total concentration of propagating free radicals in the system. Also, when a stationary state concentration of free radicals exists,

$$R_i = 2k_t[\mathrm{R} \cdot]^2 \tag{2.38}$$

Throughout this book the convention will be adopted for the description of a bimolecular reaction involving two molecules of the same reactant,

$$\mathrm{A} + \mathrm{A} = \mathrm{B} \qquad \text{Rate constant } k$$

$$\text{Rate of reaction} = \frac{\mathrm{d[B]}}{\mathrm{d}t} = k[\mathrm{A}]^2 = - \tfrac{1}{2} \frac{\mathrm{d[A]}}{\mathrm{d}t} \tag{2.39}$$

Combining equations (37) and (38) by substituting for $[\mathrm{R} \cdot]$,

$$R_p = k_p[\mathrm{M}]R_i^{1/2}/(2k_t)^{1/2} \tag{2.40}$$

The kinetic chain length ν is given by

$$\nu = \text{rate of monomer disappearance/rate of radical formation}$$

$$= - \, \mathrm{d[M]}/\mathrm{d}t/R_i = k_p[\mathrm{M}]/(2k_t)^{1/2}R_i^{1/2} \tag{2.41}$$

In order to describe the degree of polymerization it is necessary to examine the nature of the termination reaction in greater detail; and also to investigate the probability of any reaction whereby the centre of radical reactivity may be removed from a macromolecular species to a smaller molecule.

The mutual termination of two free radicals may take place by either of two mechanisms. The two unpaired electrons may undergo interaction to form a single covalent bond uniting the two original species into a single molecule. Alternatively one radical may abstract a hydrogen atom from the other so as to form two distinct molecular species, one with a terminal olefinic double bond. These two reactions are termed combination and disproportionation respectively.

$$\sim\!\mathrm{CH_2}\!-\!\mathrm{CHX} \cdot \; + \; \cdot\mathrm{CHX}\!-\!\mathrm{CH_2}\!\sim \; \rightarrow \; \sim\!\mathrm{CH_2CHX}\!-\!\mathrm{CHXCH_2}\!\sim$$
$$\text{comb. } k_{tc}$$

$$\sim\!\mathrm{CH_2}\!-\!\mathrm{CHX} \cdot \; + \; \cdot\mathrm{CHX}\!-\!\mathrm{CH_2}\!\sim \; \rightarrow \; \sim\!\mathrm{CH_2CH_2X} + \mathrm{CHX}\!=\!\mathrm{CH}\!\sim$$
$$\text{disprop. } k_{td}$$

Furthermore it is possible for a free radical to abstract a hydrogen atom from a monomolecular species such as monomer. The products of such a reaction will be inert polymer and a monomolecular free radical. Such a reaction is termed a transfer reaction. In a first simple analysis only transfer to monomer will be considered, a more detailed exposition on the effects of various other transfer reactions being given in Chapter 5.

$$R_n \cdot + M \to A_n + R \cdot \quad \text{trans. } k_f$$

where A_n represents a polymer molecule containing n monomer units. The rate of formation of polymer is given by

$$d[A]/dt = k_f[M][R \cdot] + 2k_{td}[R \cdot]^2 + k_{tc}[R \cdot]^2 \quad (2.42)$$

The instantaneous degree of polymerization is given by

$$\bar{P} = \text{rate of disappearance of monomer/rate of polymer formation}$$

$$= (-d[M]/dt)/(d[A]/dt) \quad (2.43)$$

Since the molecular weight of the polymer formed depends upon the chain length of the terminating radicals, and since at any time the polymerizing system contains growing radicals of all sizes, the degree of polymerization of the resulting polymer depends upon the probability of reaction between two radicals of a certain size. This probability depends upon the relative concentration of each size of radical. It follows therefore that the degree of polymerization of the resulting polymer will not be a single value, but some statistical distribution depending upon the radical size distribution. Consequently in any kinetic treatment involving degree of polymerization an average quantity is always involved. For convenience an average quantity will henceforth be denoted by a superscript bar. Although it is possible to average a quantity an infinite number of ways, number average, number squared average etc., in a kinetic treatment the number average degree of polymerization is involved. This may be defined as

$$\bar{P} = \sum_{i=1}^{\infty} P_i n_i / \sum_{i=1}^{\infty} n_i \quad (2.44)$$

where n_i represents the number of molecules of degree of polymerization P_i.

Combining equations (42) and (43), the inverse average instantaneous degree of polymerization is given by

$$\bar{P}^{-1} = k_f/k_p + (2k_{td} + k_{tc})[R \cdot]/k_p[M] \quad (2.45)$$

Substituting for [R·] from either equation (38) or (37)

$$\bar{P}^{-1} = k_f/k_p + (2k_{td} + k_{tc})R_i^{1/2}/(2k_{td} + 2k_{tc})^{1/2}k_p[M] \quad (2.46)$$

$$= k_f/k_p + (2k_{td} + k_{tc})R_p/k_p^2[M]^2 \quad (2.47)$$

It is usual to consider the inverse degree of polymerization, since this function exhibits a linear relationship with the rate of polymerization.

All the functions described so far represent instantaneous values of the rate of polymerization, kinetic chain length or degree of polymerization. In order to measure experimentally the last of these three, it is necessary to obtain a finite amount of polymer. It follows, therefore, that a finite decrease in monomer concentration has taken place, and the experimental value obtained represents yet a further average over the instantaneous quantities. When polymerizations are carried only to low conversions of monomer to polymer, the difference between this overall average and the instantaneous value is assumed to be negligible.

In order to investigate the distribution of degrees of polymerization in both the propagating free radicals and the resulting polymer, it is necessary to consider the differential equations describing the formation and disappearance of radicals of particular chain length.

Let the total concentration of free radicals be $[R·] = \sum_n [R_n^·]$. A great deal of confusion exists as to the appearance or non-appearance of the factor 2 in the relevant termination rate constants. Using our convention,

$$R_n^· + R_n^· \rightarrow Polymer \quad k_{tnn}$$
$$R_n^· + R_s^· \rightarrow Polymer \quad k_{tns}$$
$$k_{tnn} = \tfrac{1}{2}k_{tns}$$

Although two $R_n^·$ radicals are removed by the former reaction, the rate constant is, for statistical reasons, half the magnitude of that for the $R_n^· + R_s^·$ reaction. Thus

$$-\frac{d[R_n^·]}{dt} = k_{tns}[R_n^·] \sum_s [R_s^·] + 2k_{tnn}[R_n^·]^2 \quad n \neq s$$

$$= k_{tns}[R_n^·][R·] \quad (2.48)$$

The total rate of disappearance of all radicals is

$$2k_t[R·]^2 = -\sum_n \frac{d[R_n^·]}{dt} = \sum_n k_{tns}[R_n^·][R·]$$

whence $$k_{tns} = 2k_t \quad (2.49)$$

A general set of equations can now be formulated using the stationary state approximation

$$\frac{d[R_n^\cdot]}{dt} = 0 = k_p[M]\{[R_{n-1}^\cdot] - [R_n^\cdot]\} - [R_n^\cdot]\{k_f[M] + k_{tns}[R\cdot]\} \quad (2.50)$$

or
$$\frac{[R_n^\cdot]}{[R_{n-1}^\cdot]} = \left[1 + \frac{k_f}{k_p} + \frac{2k_t[R\cdot]}{k_p[M]}\right]^{-1} \quad (2.51)$$

Also
$$[R_1^\cdot] = R_i[k_p[M] + k_f[M] + 2k_t[R\cdot]]^{-1} \quad (2.52)$$

Multiplying together the set of n-equations which can be written from (51) and (52), the fraction of all radicals which have length, n, is

$$\frac{[R_n^\cdot]}{[R\cdot]} = \frac{2k_t[R\cdot]}{k_p[M]}\left[1 + \frac{k_f}{k_p} + \frac{2k_t[R\cdot]}{k_p[M]}\right]^{-n}$$

$$= \beta\left(1 + \beta + \frac{k_f}{k_p}\right)^{-n} \quad (2.53)$$

where
$$\beta = \frac{2k_t[R\cdot]}{k_p[M]} = \frac{2k_t R_p}{k_p^2[M]^2}$$

When n is large

$$\frac{[R_n^\cdot]}{[R\cdot]} = \beta \exp\left(-n\left[\beta + \frac{k_f}{k_p}\right]\right) \quad (2.54)$$

The radical size distribution can thus be represented by a monotonously decreasing exponential function.

The size distribution of the polymer which is formed will be determined by the radical size distribution and by the termination mechanism. For termination by combination, neglecting the transfer reaction,

$$\frac{d[A_n]}{dt} = k_{tc} \sum_{s=1}^{s=n-1} [R_{n-s}^\cdot][R_s^\cdot] \quad (2.55)$$

A factor 1/2 appears since the summation counts radicals of each size twice, but is cancelled when the substitution is made from k_{trs} to k_t.

Substituting from equation (53)

$$\frac{d[A_n]}{dt} = k_{tc}[R\cdot]^2\beta^2(1 + \beta)^{-n} \quad (2.56)$$

So that

$$\frac{d[A_n]}{-d[M]} = \tfrac{1}{2}(n - 1)\,\beta^3(1 + \beta)^{-n} \quad (2.57)$$

Which, for large values of n, can be approximated by

$$\frac{d[A_n]}{-d[M]} = \tfrac{1}{2}n\beta^3 \exp(-n\beta) \tag{2.58}$$

Consequently the mole fraction of n-mer in the polymer is

$$x_n = \frac{d[A_n]}{d[A]} = \bar{P}\tfrac{1}{2}n\beta^3 \exp(-n\beta) \tag{2.59}$$

In the absence of transfer $\bar{P}^{-1} = \tfrac{1}{2}\beta$, so that

$$x_n = \tfrac{1}{4}n\beta^2 \exp(-n\beta) \tag{2.60}$$

and the weight fraction of n-mer is

$$w_n = \tfrac{1}{4}n^2\beta^2 \exp(-n\beta) \tag{2.61}$$

When termination is by disproportionation, again neglecting transfer,

$$\frac{d[A_n]}{dt} = 2k_{td}[R_n^{\cdot}][R\cdot] \tag{2.62}$$

$$= 2k_{td}[R\cdot]^2\beta(1+\beta)^{-n} \tag{2.63}$$

Continuing, as in the previous case,

$$\frac{d[A_n]}{d[M]} = \beta^2(1+\beta)^{-n} \tag{2.64}$$

Which, for large n, becomes

$$\frac{d[A_n]}{d[M]} = \beta^2 \exp(-n\beta) \tag{2.65}$$

In this case $\bar{P}^{-1} = \beta$, and the mole fraction of n-mer is

$$x_n = \beta \exp(-n\beta) \tag{2.66}$$

The weight fraction is

$$\omega_n = n\beta \exp(-n\beta) \tag{2.67}$$

In the case of a polymerization carried to low conversion of monomer to polymer, $\bar{P}$ and β are essentially constant, whereupon the size distribution of the resulting polymer can be represented by a simple exponential function.

The distribution functions derived above illustrate the application of kinetic methods to an idealized system. The derivation of distribution functions for more complex systems and the use of statistical methods are dealt with in another volume of this series.

The Chain Length–Radical Reactivity Approximation

The kinetic treatment given above contained two vital simplifying assumptions. The first of these was that for high molecular weight radicals the radical reactivity is essentially independent of the chain length. It is certainly to be expected that changes in radical reactivity will get progressively smaller as larger chains are considered, but it has also been shown that differences between the concentrations of n-mer become progressively smaller as n becomes very large. Consequently even small differences in reactivity might be important when consideration is made over a range of chain lengths which vary appreciably in concentration.

There are two important situations which arise in practice when this approximation will not be valid. The first case is when polymerization is initiated by a radical containing groups which exert powerful inductive or electromeric effects, and low molecular weight polymer is formed. These polar effects will influence the reactivity of the propagating free radical to a decreasing extent as the distance between the group and the radical increases. Furthermore, because of the well-known 6-number, it might be expected that the radical containing an initiator fragment and two monomer residues would have an anomalous reactivity. This first case is essentially a chemical effect and approximate allowance for it may be made by assuming that the propagation and termination reactions will be affected in a related way. The relationship commonly used assumes that the termination rate constant is the product of two parts, each descriptive of the chain length of one of the radicals involved, and that the magnitude of each factor varies with chain length in exactly the same way as does the propagation rate constant.

$$k_{tr,s} = k_r k_s, \quad k_{pr}/k_r = \delta \tag{2.68}$$

where δ is a constant. Although it is likely that neither the factorization nor the proportionality are correct, they at least represent a simple reactivity dependence on chain length. Again the stationary state equation governing the concentration of n-mer is, neglecting transfer reactions,

$$0 = d[R_n^{\cdot}]/dt = [M](k_{p,n-1}[R_{n-1}^{\cdot}] - k_{p,n}[R_n^{\cdot}]) - [R_n^{\cdot}]\sum_{s=1}^{\infty} k_{t,ns}[R_s^{\cdot}]$$

$$= [M](k_{p,n-1}[R_{n-1}^{\cdot}] - k_{p,n}[R_n^{\cdot}]) - k_n[R_n^{\cdot}]\sum_{s=1}^{\infty} k_s[R_s^{\cdot}]$$

$$\tag{2.69}$$

Adding the infinite set of such equations

$$R_i = \sum_{s=1}^{\infty} \left(k_n[\mathrm{R}_n^{\cdot}] \sum_{s=1}^{\infty} k_s[\mathrm{R}_s^{\cdot}] \right) \tag{2.70}$$

It is usual to equate the double sum to a perfect square when

$$R_i = \left(\sum_{s=1}^{\infty} k_s[\mathrm{R}_s^{\cdot}] \right)^2 \tag{2.71}$$

Now
$$R_p = [\mathrm{M}] \sum_{s=1}^{\infty} k_{p,s}[\mathrm{R}_s^{\cdot}] \tag{2.72}$$

$$= \delta M \sum_{s=1}^{\infty} k_s[\mathrm{R}_s^{\cdot}] = \delta M R_i^{1/2} \tag{2.73}$$

which is an equation of the same form as equation (40).

The second situation when the rate constants for one or more of the steps of the polymerization are not independent of the size of the free radicals involved arises when one or both of the termination and propagation reactions are diffusion-controlled.

Over a rather wide range of solution viscosity the transport processes of macromolecules are slower than the radical termination reaction, but the propagation reaction is slower than the diffusion of monomer molecules. Under these circumstances it is likely that the propagation rate constant is virtually independent of the radical chain length, whereas the termination rate constant will exhibit a complex dependence on radical size. The relation between the diffusion-controlled termination rate constant and radical chain length depends on the nature of the diffusive processes involved, but is essentially a sum of two functions, and not a product as assumed in the previous treatment. There is evidence[3] to suggest that most polymerization reactions are characterized by a diffusion-controlled termination process even in a normal liquid phase polymerization carried to low conversion. Consequently the limitations of the simple kinetic relationship must always be borne in mind.

In very viscous media it is possible that both the termination and the propagation reactions are diffusion-controlled. However, even under these conditions a factorized termination rate constant and the propagation rate constant will not exhibit the same chain length dependence, since in the case of propagation monomer diffusion is most important.

The Stationary State Approximation

The second vital approximation which appeared in the foregoing derivations was one which is used in the kinetic treatment of almost all reactions involving intermediate species of high reactivity. The Bodenstein stationary state assumption is a particularly powerful kinetic tool, because by its use differential equations, some of which may be insoluble, can be converted to algebraic equalities. The simplification gained by such a process is so attractive that the approximation might be applied under circumstances when it is not strictly valid. It is beneficial, therefore, to consider in greater detail the conditions attached to this approximation.

In any reaction where an intermediate, A, is formed at a rate, R_i, and disappears either by reaction with a terminating molecule, or by a mutual interaction of two intermediates at a rate R_t

$$d[A]/dt = R_i - R_t = R_i - nk[X]^m[A]^n \qquad (2.74)$$

where k is the rate constant describing the termination reaction, $[X]$ and $[A]$ are the concentrations of the terminating agent and reactive species respectively, and m and n are the kinetic orders for these species. Integration of equation (74) yields the boundary conditions, $d[A]/dt = R_i$ at $t = 0$ and $d[A]/dt = 0$ at $t = \infty$ if R_i and $[X]$ are assumed to be constant. Obviously $d[A]/dt$ can never be exactly zero, more especially since over a large time the concentrations of the initiating and terminating molecules cannot remain constant.

However, within the limits of accuracy of any experimental study, it is possible that $d[A]/dt$ is negligible compared with both the rate of initiation and the rate of termination. Then $R_i = R_t + d[A]/dt \sim R_t$. This gives a more fundamental criterion for the application of the stationary state approximation than the direct equality $d[A]/dt = 0$. The errors arising in a calculated value of the concentration of intermediate by use of the approximation $d[A]/dt \ll R_i$ can be obtained from the ratio of the correct to the approximated value $[A]/[A]_s$ where $[A]_s$ is the value calculated using the stationary state assumption. Integration of equation (74), for the particular example of second order termination of reactive intermediates, yields

$$\ln\left\{\frac{(R_i/nk[X]^m)^{1/2} + [A]}{(R_i/nk[X]^m)^{1/2} - [A]}\right\} = 2(R_i nk[X]^m)^{1/2}t \qquad (2.75)$$

and when the stationary state assumption has been made

$$[A]_s = (R_i/nk[X]^m)^{1/2} \qquad (2.76)$$

whereupon substitution gives

$$[A]/[A_s] = \tanh\{(nR_ik[X]^m)^{1/2}t\} \tag{2.77}$$

For $[A]/[A_s]$ to be $\sim$ unity $(nR_ik[X]^m)^{1/2}t \gg 1$

or $$t_s \gg (nR_ik[X]^m)^{-1/2} \tag{2.78}$$

where t_s is the time required for the concentration of intermediate to reach an "equilibrium" concentration within the limits of the approximation.

In any real system the concentration of initiator and of terminating agent must decrease during the reaction, and the idealized condition derived above is not a sufficient justification for the application of the stationary state approximation. The physical significance of any extension to the necessary condition, $d[A]/dt \ll R_i$, is that the concentration of the reactive intermediate must reach its equilibrium "stationary" value for each value of the concentration of initiator or terminating agent. Any change in the concentration of these reagents must take place over times which are very large compared with the times required for the concentration of reactive intermediate to reach its "stationary" value, i.e. dt/dR_i, $dt/dR_t \gg t_s$.

Again for the particular example of second order termination of reactive intermediate,

$$\frac{dt}{R_i} \gg t_s \gg (nR_ik[X]^m)^{-1/2} \tag{2.79}$$

If initiation involves l molecules of initiator to produce j molecules of reactive intermediate,

$$\frac{dR_i}{dt} = -\frac{l^2R_i^2}{j[I]} \tag{2.80}$$

whereupon the condition for application of the approximation may be formulated as

$$\left|\frac{l^2R_i^2}{j[I]}\right| \ll (R_ink[X]^m)^{1/2}$$

$$nk[X]^m \gg \frac{l^4R_i^3}{j^2[I]^2} \tag{2.81}$$

For the particular case of free radical polymerization, l is usually 1, j is 2, m is zero and $nk = 2k_t$ and R_i can be replaced by $2k_i[I]$. The conditions for the application of the stationary state approximation may be listed as $d[R\cdot]/dt \ll R_i$ which is the same as $t \gg (R_i 2k_t)^{-1/2}$ where t is the time over which an observation is carried out. Combining this with the condition governing the rate of disappearance of initiator, the general condition is $k_t \gg k_i^3[I]$, $(4k_i[I]t^2)^{-1}$.

The conditions governing the application of the assumption to reactions where the disappearance of active species is not second order in that species, or where the change in concentration in some other reactant must be considered, can be investigated in the same fashion.

REFERENCES

1. BENSON, S. W., *The Foundations of Chemical Kinetics*, McGraw-Hill, New York (1960).
2. RABINOWITCH, E., *Trans. Faraday Soc.*, 1937, **33**, 1225.
3. NORTH, A. M., *Progress in High Polymers*, ed. by PEAKER, F. W. and ROBB, J. C., Heywood, Chapter V.

CHAPTER 3

THE DETERMINATION OF INDIVIDUAL
RATE CONSTANTS

THE aim of any kinetic study of a chemical reaction is the elucidation of the mechanism of the reaction, followed by a correlation of the reactivities of the species involved with their chemical structure. The most convenient method of achieving this second purpose is by measurement of the rate constants of the various steps involved in the overall transformation of reactants to products. Expression of any rate constant in an Arrhenius form may then yield information on the enthalpy and entropy changes involved during the formation of a transition state as two molecules react.

In common with other chain reactions, free radical polymerizations involve several rate constants, and the determination of the individual values necessitates a detailed study of several features of the polymerization.

The Observable Features of a Polymerization

The most easily observed property of any polymerization is the rate of reaction, usually defined as the rate of disappearance of monomer. Because of the chemical and physical differences between double and single carbon to carbon bonds, this rate may be followed by a variety of methods.

The amount of polymer formed may be determined gravimetrically or the monomer remaining titrated with bromine. Both of these methods require sampling techniques, and in many cases it is simpler to observe the change in a physical property resulting from the saturation of the olefinic double bond. Changes in specific volume, refractive index, dielectric constant or viscosity are all observable in isothermal systems, while under adiabatic conditions the heat evolved by the exothermic addition reaction may also provide a measure of the rate of reaction.

The second property of a chain reaction which can be measured is the kinetic chain length. This is the number of monomer molecules consumed per free radical formed in the initiation reaction. While observation of the number of monomer molecules converted to polymer is relatively simple, chemical analysis of the number of initiating fragments incorporated in polymer is rather difficult. The use of radioactive initiators, however, does enable accurate determination of this quantity to be made.

The third observable feature of any polymerization is the degree of polymerization defined as the number of monomer units linked together in each polymer chain. In the absence of transfer reactions, this is equal to the kinetic chain length, but otherwise must be smaller. The molecular weight of the polymer molecules may be measured using techniques such as study of colligative effects, light scattering or solution viscosity, or by analytical measurements of the number of chains present in any polymer sample.

Equations Relating these Observable Properties

Equations relating the various observable quantities of a polymerization reaction to the rate constants of the various steps have been derived in Chapter 2. The general forms of these equations were:

$$R_p = \frac{k_p}{(2k_t)^{1/2}} R_i^{1/2}[M] \tag{3.1}$$

$$\bar{P}^{-1} = \frac{k_f}{k_p} + \frac{(2k_t)^{1/2} R_i^{1/2}}{k_p[M]} \quad \text{(disproportionation)} \tag{3.2}$$

$$\nu = \frac{k_p[M]}{(2k_t)^{1/2} R_i^{1/2}} \tag{3.3}$$

All these equations have two common unknowns, $k_p/(2k_t)^{1/2}$ and R_i, while equation (2) has the third unknown, k_f/k_p. Consequently the knowledge of R_i and one value of either the rate of polymerization or the kinetic chain length, allows immediate evaluation of the ratio $k_p/(2k_t)^{1/2}$. The knowledge of at least two values of the rate of initiation and the corresponding values of the degree of polymerization, yields both the ratios $k_p/(2k_t)^{1/2}$ and k_f/k_p. The use of any one of these equations then depends upon the evaluation of the rate of initiation, and no matter which equation is used, it is possible only to evaluate certain ratios of rate constants and not the individual constants themselves.

Measurement of the Rate of Initiation

It is possible to treat any two of the equations (1) to (3) as simultaneous equations in the two unknowns, R_i and $kp/(2k_t)^{1/2}$. Combination of the two equations can be made so as to eliminate either unknown.

As an example, equations (1) and (2) may be combined to give

$$\bar{P}^{-1} = \frac{k_f}{k_p} + \frac{2k_t}{k_p^2[M]^2} \times R_p \tag{3.4}$$

$$\bar{P}^{-1} = \frac{k_f}{k_p} + \frac{R_i}{R_p} \tag{3.5}$$

A plot of inverse degree of polymerization against rate of polymerization has intercept k_f/k_p and slope $2k_t/k_p^2[M]^2$. Substitution in either equation (1) or equation (5) yields the rate of initiation. In the same way combination of equations (1) and (2) yields the simple relationship

$$R_i = R_p/\nu \tag{3.6}$$

It is possible to measure the rate of initiation by means other than the simultaneous determination of two quantities fitting the equations detailed above. The simplest method involves measurement of the inhibition time in the presence of a free radical scavenger, so that the rate of consumption of inhibitor is known. This rate is r^{-1} times the rate of initiation where r is the number of free radicals removed by each inhibitor molecule.

$$R_i = r[I]/t_i \tag{3.7}$$

where t_i is the "inhibition time" and [I] is the concentration of inhibitor. The difficulty inherent in this determination is the assignment of a value to t_i. This arises because at very low concentrations of inhibitor, the polymerization reaction is not completely inhibited, and the reaction rate progressively increases. The kinetic treatment of this phenomenon is discussed in Chapter 5.

Knowledge of the rate of initiation can be used to determine the rate constant of the initiation reaction,

$$R_i = fk_i[X]^n \tag{3.8}$$

where n is the order of the reaction in the initiating species, X, and f is the efficiency of the radicals produced in starting growing polymer chains. Since it is often possible to follow the rate of disappearance of initiator, the rate of initiation allows evaluation of the efficiency, f.

The rate of initiation, when combined with the value of one other observable property, can therefore yield fk_i, k_f/k_p and $k_p/(2k_t)^{1/2}$. In order to obtain individual values of the propagation, transfer and termination rate constants it is necessary to consider some further property of the system. The determination of just one of the individual constants can be used to yield the individual values of all the constants.

Measurement of Radical Concentrations

When the polymer chain length is very large, monomer disappearance is predominantly due to the propagation reaction, and

$$-\frac{d[M]}{dt} = R_p = k_p[M][R\cdot] \tag{3.9}$$

Measurement of R_p and the radical concentration, $[R\cdot]$, would then yield a value for k_p, which could then be used in conjunction with the ratios of rate constants already described to derive k_t and k_f.

Unfortunately in most common polymerization systems the concentration of free radicals is very low, about 10^{-8} moles l^{-1} and beyond the sensitivity of most methods of measurement. At the present time refined techniques of electron spin resonance spectroscopy are theoretically capable of measuring concentrations down to 10^{-11} moles l^{-1}, and so can be used in those polymerizations which contain radical concentrations greater than this limit. The majority of electron spin resonance spectrometers in use, however, are unable to measure accurately free radical concentrations below 10^{-7} moles l^{-1}.

When polymerizations are carried out in viscous media, or in solvents which precipitate the polymer, the termination reaction is greatly reduced because of the inability of two radicals to diffuse together and undergo mutual termination. Under these circumstances the radical concentration may be high enough to be measured by most electron spin resonance spectrometers, and evaluation of the individual rate constants follows directly.

Study of the polymerization of most common monomers in normal solutions, therefore, still requires a rather involved investigation of further properties of the system in order to evaluate the individual values of the rate constants.

Radical Lifetime Determinations

The average lifetime of the kinetic chain, τ, during stationary state conditions is given by

$$\tau = (2R_i k_t)^{-1/2} \tag{3.10}$$

Substitution of equation (1) yields

$$\tau = k_p[M]/2k_t R_p \tag{3.11}$$

Then any measurement of the radical lifetime, in conjunction with the rate of polymerization can yield the ratio k_p/k_t. Comparison of the values of $k_p/2k_t$ and $k_p/(2k_t)^{1/2}$ immediately allows evaluation of the individual constants.

Unfortunately a direct evaluation of τ during stationary state conditions is not possible. It is possible, however, to obtain values for the radical lifetime, and hence for k_p/k_t, under conditions when the concentration of free radicals in the system is undergoing some change to, or from, stationary state conditions. In other words a study of the non-stationary state of a polymerization, in conjunction with a study of the stationary state, yields two different ratios of rate constants, which then allow evaluation of the individual constants.

(a) The Technique of Intermittent Illumination[1]

The most widely used method of obtaining radical lifetimes is by intermittent illumination of a photosensitized polymerization. Because illumination is usually interrupted by rotation of a disc with sector-shaped apertures, this experimental method is often referred to as the Rotating Sector Technique.

As the illumination is interrupted, the radical concentration and rate of polymerization falls and rises, so that over many interruptions it is possible to measure a constant average rate of polymerization. The technique is, nonetheless, based upon the behaviour of the non-stationary phases of the free radical concentration.

When a system is exposed to intermittent illumination with the dark periods long enough to allow termination of all radicals formed during the light period (dark times longer than the radical lifetimes), then the light periods may be considered as separate. If these light periods last a fraction $1/n$ of the total duration of the reaction, the average rate of the reaction will be $1/n$ of the rate for constant illumination.

Under the alternative conditions when the dark periods are so short that only a small fraction of the radicals formed in the light period can terminate, the rate of reaction during the dark period does not differ significantly from that during the light period. If the light periods are also short, the radical concentration can neither rise nor fall to the extreme values experienced for longer light and dark times. The reaction then involves a pseudo-stationary state concentration of free radicals and the rate of initiation is dependent upon an intensity of illumination $1/n$ of that experienced during uninterrupted photopolymerization. The change from light and dark intervals greater than the radical lifetime to intervals much less than the radical lifetimes is easily made by increasing the speed of the rotating sector.

When the rate of initiation is directly proportional to the intensity of illumination, and when the rate of polymerization is proportional to the rate of initiation to some power, x, the rate of polymerization for very short light and dark times is $(1/n)^x$ of the rate for constant illumination.

Two cases are illustrated in Fig. 3.1 as a plot of radical concentration, or rate of polymerization, against time. So long as x is not unity, the average rates for high and low sector speeds will differ, the change from one value to the other occurring when the dark times are approximately equal to the radical lifetime.

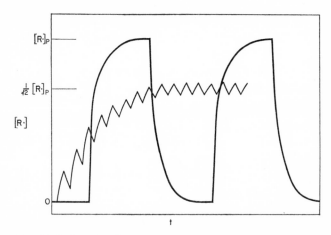

Fig. 3.1. Variation of radical concentration with time at fast, and slow, sector speeds. $[\text{R} \cdot]_p$ is the photo-stationary concentration.

The method is only of use if the rate of reaction is not proportional to the first power of the rate of initiation. For any chain reaction of large kinetic chain length this implies that the propagation and termination reactions must not be of the same order in the reactive species. Although this is a severe limitation in the case of many gas-phase reactions, most polymerization reactions in the liquid phase exhibit a propagation reaction which is first order in free radicals, and a termination reaction which is second order. For purely second order radical termination, x is $1/2$.

In order to evaluate $k_p/2k_t$ or τ more precisely, a rather more fundamental kinetic analysis of the technique is required. The simplest system which can be studied is a polymerization in which the only initiation is photosensitized, but in which light absorption is negligible.

Under these conditions there is no initiation during the dark periods, and the rate of initiation is uniform throughout the system.

If termination occurs by mutual interaction of two free radicals, the stationary state concentration of radicals under steady illumination is

$$[R\cdot]_s = \left(\frac{R_i}{2k_t}\right)^{1/2}$$

and the corresponding rate of polymerization,

$$R_{p,s} = k_p[M]R_i^{1/2}/(2k_t)^{1/2} \tag{3.12}$$

During the light periods the increase in the radical concentration is given by

$$\frac{d[R\cdot]}{dt} = R_i - 2k_t[R\cdot]^2 \tag{3.13}$$

which, upon integration, gives

$$\left(\frac{2k_t}{R_i}\right)^{1/2} \tanh^{-1}\left[\left(\frac{2k_t}{R_i}\right)^{1/2}[R\cdot]\right] = 2k_t t + C_l \tag{3.14}$$

and substituting from equation (12)

$$\frac{1}{[R\cdot]_s} \tanh^{-1}\frac{[R\cdot]}{[R\cdot]_s} = 2k_t t + C_l \tag{3.15}$$

Correspondingly, during the dark periods,

$$\frac{d[R\cdot]}{dt} = -2k_t[R\cdot]^2 \tag{3.16}$$

and

$$\frac{1}{[R\cdot]} = 2k_t t + C_d \tag{3.17}$$

in which C_l and C_d are constants of integration.

During the pseudo-stationary condition under which the increase in radical concentration during the light period exactly balances the decrease during the dark period, the average radical concentration does not change. If $[R]_1$ and $[R]_2$ represent the concentration of radicals at the beginning and end, respectively, of each dark period, and if t_l and

pt_l represent the times of the light and dark periods respectively, the average concentration during the light period is

$$[\bar{R}\cdot]_l = \frac{1}{t_l} \int_{\text{light}} [R\cdot]dt = \frac{1}{4k_t t_l} \ln \left\{ \frac{1 - \left(\frac{[R\cdot]_1}{[R\cdot]_s} \right)^2}{1 - \left(\frac{[R\cdot]_2}{[R\cdot]_s} \right)^2} \right\} \qquad (3.18)$$

and during the dark period

$$[\bar{R}\cdot]_d = \frac{1}{pt_l} \int_{\text{dark}} [R\cdot]dt = \frac{1}{4k_t pt_l} \ln \left(\frac{[R\cdot]_1}{[R\cdot]_2} \right)^2 \qquad (3.19)$$

The average concentration over a complete cycle, light and dark, is

$$[\bar{R}\cdot] = ([\bar{R}\cdot]_l + p[\bar{R}\cdot]_d)/(p + 1) \qquad (3.20)$$

From (15) and (17)

$$\tanh^{-1} \frac{[R\cdot]_1}{[R\cdot]_s} - \tanh^{-1} \frac{[R\cdot]_2}{[R\cdot]_s} = 2[R\cdot]_s k_t t_l = (2R_i k_t)^{1/2} t_l \qquad (3.21)$$

and

$$\frac{1}{[R\cdot]_2} - \frac{1}{[R\cdot]_1} = 2k_t pt_l \qquad (3.22)$$

Combining equations (18) to (22), and eliminating $[R\cdot]_2$

$$\frac{[\bar{R}\cdot]}{[R\cdot]_s} = \frac{1}{p + 1} \left\{ 1 + \frac{1}{b} \ln \left(1 + \frac{pb}{1 + [R\cdot]_s/[R\cdot]_1} \right) \right\} \qquad (3.23)$$

where $b = (2R_i k_t)^{1/2}t$ and

$$\frac{[R\cdot]_1}{[R\cdot]_s} = \frac{1}{2(pb + \tanh b)} \{pb \tanh b + [p^2 b^2 \tanh^2 b + 4(pb + \tanh b)$$

$$\tanh b]^{1/2}\} \qquad (3.24)$$

Under stationary state illumination,

$$\tau_s = (2k_t[R\cdot]_s)^{-1} \qquad (3.25)$$

So that $b = t_l/\tau_s$.

Substitution of equation (24) in equation (23) yields the general equation for the ratio $[\bar{\mathrm{R}}\cdot]/[\mathrm{R}\cdot]_s$ in terms of the parameters p and b only.

$$\frac{[\bar{\mathrm{R}}\cdot]}{[\mathrm{R}\cdot]_s} = \frac{1}{p+1}\left\{1 + \frac{1}{b}\ln\right.$$

$$\left.\left[1 + \frac{p^2b^2\tanh b + pb(p^2b^2\tanh^2 b + 4\{pb + \tanh b\}\tanh b)^{1/2}}{pb\tanh b + pb(p^2b^2\tanh^2 b + 4\{pb + \tanh b\}\tanh b)^{1/2} + 2(pb + \tanh b)}\right]\right\}$$

$$(3.26)$$

Equation (26) is itself rather unwieldy to be repeatedly used for determination of b. It is more convenient to use curves plotted on the basis of equation (26). This may conveniently be accomplished experimentally by obtaining a number of results with different sector speeds and ratios of light to dark times. Plots of the ratio of intermittent to

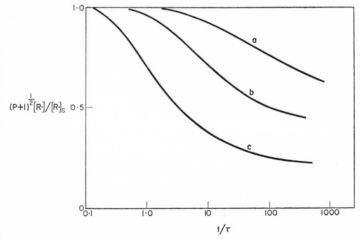

FIG. 3.2. Dependence of the normalized relative mean radical concentration on the ratio time of illumination to radical lifetime: dark to light ratio
(a) 1; (b) 3; (c) 15.

continuous rates (normalized by the factor $(p + 1)^{1/2}$), against $\ln t_l$ are then superimposed on a series of curves drawn from equation (26) (Fig. 3.2) and shifted horizontally until the best fit with the curve for the appropriate value of p is found. The value of $1/\tau$ is then obtained directly.

In this treatment the kinetic analysis has been carried out on an idealized system with no dark initiation, uniform light absorption, a termination reaction second order in free radicals and with an instantaneous change from light to dark. The technique has been extended to cover cases not governed by all these conditions and the relevant procedures along with the references to the original publications are listed in the comprehensive text by Burnett.[2]

One of the experimental advantages of the use of intermittent illumination is that the rate measurements are averaged over a time very much greater than the radical lifetime, and because of this (and the fact that a constant average radical concentration is observed) the method is often referred to as a pseudo-stationary state measurement.

(b) *The Flow Technique*[3]

Radical lifetimes may be obtained by use of a flow technique; another method which does not suffer from the necessity of taking observations over very short times. The basis of the method is a measurement of the time taken for a stream of monomer to fall freely from an initiating region of intense illumination into an efficiently stirred bath of some terminating agent. For short times of fall radicals do not undergo self-termination. Consequently as the time of fall is increased both the yield and molecular weight of polymer increase. When the time of fall is greater than the radical lifetime, further increases in flow time produce no effect upon the yield or molecular weight of the polymer. The method is, of course, applicable to flow along a tube as well as to free fall, except that under these conditions turbulence and slow-flow at the tube wall introduce spurious complications.

This method has the advantage over the sector technique that the order of the termination reaction with respect to the free radicals is immaterial.

Consider again the ideal case of a monomer which undergoes initiation only when illuminated, and when termination in the bath is instantaneous.

Let the time spent by any small volume element of monomer in the illumination zone be t_l.

In the light zone,

$$\frac{d[\text{R}\cdot]}{dt} = R_i - 2k_t[\text{R}\cdot]^2 \tag{3.13}$$

and

$$\frac{1}{[\text{R}\cdot]_s} \tanh^{-1} \frac{[\text{R}\cdot]}{[\text{R}\cdot]_s} = 2k_t t_l + C_l \tag{3.15}$$

so
$$[R \cdot] = [R \cdot]_s \tanh \frac{t_l}{\tau} \qquad (3.27)$$

If F_1 is the fraction of monomer polymerized during illumination,

$$F_1 = \int_0^{t_l} - \frac{d[M]}{dt} \times \frac{dt}{[M]} \qquad (3.28)$$

which in combination with (27), for small values of F_1, reduces to

$$F_1 = \frac{k_p}{2k_t} \ln \left\{ \cosh \frac{t_l}{\tau} \right\} \qquad (3.29)$$

Out of the illumination zone,

$$[R \cdot] = [R \cdot]_m / (1 + 2k_t [R \cdot]_m t) \qquad (3.30)$$

where $[R \cdot]_m$ is the maximum concentration of free radicals formed during illumination. Then the fraction of monomer polymerized during free fall is

$$F_2 = \int_0^{t_d} - \frac{d[M]}{dt} \times \frac{dt}{[M]} \qquad (3.28)$$

where t_d is the time lapse between illumination and termination. Upon introduction of equation (30),

$$F_2 = \frac{k_p}{2k_t} \ln \left(1 + \frac{t_d}{\tau} \tanh \frac{t_l}{\tau} \right) \qquad (3.31)$$

The total fraction of monomer polymerized is thus

$$F_T = \frac{k_p}{2k_t} \ln \left\{ \cosh \frac{t_l}{\tau} \left[1 + \frac{t_d}{\tau} \tanh \frac{t_l}{\tau} \right] \right\} \qquad (3.32)$$

For dark times much less than radical lifetimes,

$$F_T = \frac{k_p}{2k_t} \ln \cosh \frac{t_l}{\tau} \qquad (3.33)$$

from which $k_p/2k_t$ and τ can be found directly.

The principal disadvantage of this method is the difficulty in measuring the small yields of polymer obtained. This is especially the case for very short flow times.

(c) *Non-stationary State Measurements*

The direct method of ascertaining radical lifetimes is observation of the non-stationary state phases of the polymerization. It is possible to study the build-up of the radical concentration during the initial stages of the reaction, or the decay of the radical concentration upon cessation or reduction of initiation. The principal experimental difficulties of these studies arise because of the rather short times available for this type of measurement.

During the initial stages of a polymerization the conditions governing the concentration of free radicals are,

$$\frac{d[R\cdot]}{dt} = R_i - 2k_t[R\cdot]^2 \tag{3.13}$$

and hence

$$[R\cdot]/[R\cdot]_s = \tanh\frac{t}{\tau} \tag{3.34}$$

Although this equation can be used directly to find τ, it is often more convenient to use the fraction of monomer converted to polymer,

$$F = \frac{k_p}{2k_t}\ln\cosh\frac{t}{\tau} \tag{3.35}$$

which, when the stationary state is achieved, reduces to

$$F = \frac{k_p}{2k_t}\left(\frac{t}{\tau} - \ln 2\right) \tag{3.36}$$

Then a plot of fraction of monomer converted to polymer against time has as asymptote a straight line of slope $k_p/2k_t$ and intercept $\tau \ln 2$.

In the case of a photosensitized reaction, upon cessation of illumination,

$$\frac{1}{R_p} - \frac{1}{R_{p,0}} = \frac{2k_t}{k_p[M]}t \tag{3.37}$$

where $R_{p,0}$ is the rate of polymerization before irradiation is cut off at the time, $t = 0$. A plot of inverse rate of polymerization against time yields $k_p/2k_t$.

In cases where a constant dark rate of initiation remains after cessation of the photosensitized reaction,

$$\frac{d[R\cdot]}{dt} = R_{i,d} - 2k_t[R\cdot]^2 \tag{3.13}$$

where $R_{i,d}$ is the rate of "dark" initiation, and integration yields

$$\frac{1}{[\text{R} \cdot]_d} \left(\tanh^{-1} \frac{[\text{R} \cdot]}{[\text{R} \cdot]_d} - \tanh^{-1} \frac{[\text{R} \cdot]_0}{[\text{R} \cdot]_d} \right) = 2k_t t \tag{3.38}$$

where $[\text{R} \cdot]_d$ and $[\text{R} \cdot]_0$ are radical concentrations at infinite and zero times respectively, i.e. concentrations associated with the stationary state rates of dark and illuminated polymerizations. Thus

$$\tanh^{-1} \frac{R_p}{R_{p,0}} = \tanh^{-1} \frac{R_{p,0}}{R_{p,d}} + \frac{2k_t}{k_p[\text{M}]} R_{p,d} t \tag{3.39}$$

where R_p, $R_{p,d}$ and $R_{p,0}$ are the rates of polymerization at time t, and at infinite and zero times respectively. A plot of $\tanh^{-1} R_p/R_{p,d}$ against time then yields $k_p/2k_t$.

Several methods exist for the measurement of the rate of polymerization during the non-stationary state. The most straightforward involve the determination of the temperature rise[4] during adiabatic polymerizations for which the heat of polymerization is known. This rise may be observed by direct measurement, or by means of a secondary effect such as thermal expansion.

It is also possible to study the rate under almost isothermal conditions using recording equipment and making allowances for departure from ideal isothermal behaviour. In fact, solution of the simultaneous differential equations describing heat flow and free radical concentration yields the ratio $k_p/2k_t$ under conditions which are not isothermal.[5] The temperature effect, by extending the time over which the effects of the non-stationary state are observable in fact facilitates the measurement.

(d) *The Viscosity Method*[6]

Because the presence of small amounts of high polymer may exert a considerable effect upon the viscosity of a system, the observation of viscosity may provide accurate information on the amount of polymer present. By studying the changes in viscosity over stationary and non-stationary phases of the polymerization it is possible to obtain values of the individual rate constants provided a relationship is known between the viscosity and the molecular weight of the polymer which is formed. It is also possible to correlate a study of the viscosity changes during a photo after-effect with other observations of the stationary state in order to obtain the individual constants.

Despite the simplicity of the experimenal observations the theoretical treatment is complex. The original kinetic scheme was based upon the formation of diradicals during initiation and termination by disproportionation, and it is this scheme which is reproduced in most textbooks. Modification of the scheme to cover monoradical initiation and termination by combination has been published. For the detailed kinetic expressions the reader is referred to the original publications. In point of fact the method is now seldom used for the determination of rate constants.

REFERENCES

1. BRIERS, F., CHAPMAN, D. L., and WALTERS, E., *J. chem. Soc.*, 1926, 562; NOYES, W. A. and LEIGHTON, P. A., *The Photochemistry of Gases*, Reinhold, New York (1941).
2. BURNETT, G. M., *Mechanism of Polymer Reactions*, Interscience, New York (1954); BURNETT, G. M. and MELVILLE, H. W., in *Investigation of Rates and Mechanisms of Reactions (Technique of Organic Chemistry*, Vol. VIII), ed. by WEISSBERGER, A. and FREISS, S., Interscience, New York (1953), Chapter III.
3. HICKS, J. A. and MELVILLE, H. W., *Proc. roy. Soc.*, 1954, **A226**, 314; GOLDFINGER, G. and HEFFELFINGER, C., *J. Polymer Sci.*, 1954, **13**, 123; FUNT, B. L. and COLLINS, E., *J. Polymer Sci.*, 1958, **28**, 97.
4. BENGOUGH, W. I. and MELVILLE, H. W., *Proc. roy. Soc.*, 1954, **A225**, 330; 1955, **A230**, 429; BENGOUGH, W. I., *Trans. Faraday Soc.*, 1958, **54**, 54.
5. BENSON, S. W. and NORTH, A. M., *J. Amer. chem. Soc.*, 1958, **80**, 5625.
6. BAMFORD, C. H. and DEWAR, M. J. S., *Proc. roy. Soc.*, 1948, **A192**, 309.

CHAPTER 4

RADICAL-FORMING REACTIONS

THE formation of free radicals in a polymerization system may usually proceed by any of three processes. These are spontaneous or thermal reaction of monomer molecules, exposure of monomer to a variety of different radiations, or homolytic decomposition of some other molecule, an initiator, sometimes referred to rather inaccurately as a catalyst.

Thermal Initiation

The ability to polymerize spontaneously in the absence of other initiating species or in the absence of irradiation is not possessed by all ethylenic monomers. One monomer which does exhibit appreciable and reproducible rates of thermal polymerization is styrene.

The precise mechanism of the thermal polymerization of styrene is still somewhat obscure. The original suggestion by Flory[1] was that a bimolecular reaction involved the combination of two monomer units to form an $\alpha\omega$ diradical, propagation of which then proceeded at both reactive ends.

$$2CH_2{=}CHX \rightarrow \cdot CHXCH_2CH_2CHX \cdot$$

This reaction was held to be more probable energetically than the disproportionation reaction to two monoradicals

$$2CH_2{=}CHX \rightarrow CH_3CHX \cdot + CH_2{=}CX \cdot$$

A detailed kinetic examination[2] of the thermal polymerization of styrene, however, proved that the propagation step took place by reaction of monoradicals with monomer. Furthermore, Haward[3] calculated that for any diradical, an intramolecular termination reaction would occur before any chain growth.

In order to explain the formation of monoradicals Mayo[4] has postulated a termolecular reaction,

$$3CH_2{=}CHX \rightarrow CH_3CHX \cdot + CH_3CX{=}CHCHX \cdot$$

The dimeric product of this reaction was assumed to have additional conjugation and resonance stabilization compared with the diradical

36

postulated by Flory. The rarity of termolecular reactions in solution might then explain the fact that few monomers undergo this spontaneous initiation.

Measurements[5] of the rate of formation of free radicals by consumption of diphenylpicrylhydrazyl have yielded values much greater than those calculated from rates of polymerization. This suggests that the majority of free radicals terminate before yielding high polymers in accord with the formation of diradicals, only a small fraction of which undergo a transfer reaction to become propagating monoradicals.

Although the rate of polymerization should be second order in monomer for bimolecular initiation, and five-halves order for termolecular initiation, a straightforward determination of the overall order of the polymerization with respect to monomer has not yet resolved the ambiguity. This is mainly because only a small fraction of the radicals do propagate, and because of the influence of other reactions. Studies on the initiation by substances known to form monoradicals have shown that the majority of radicals formed do propagate polymerization, so that the inefficiency of the thermal initiation process does seem to be evidence for the bimolecular reaction.

Initiation by Irradiation

Free radicals may be obtained when a polymerization system is irradiated with ultraviolet light, or when the system is exposed to any ionizing radiation. As the mechanism of initiation is not the same in each case, it is advantageous to consider each type of radiation separately.

The mechanism of photochemical initiation, like thermal initiation, is still somewhat obscure. Many workers have postulated that the absorption of energy by the double bond of the monomer leads to the excitation of the π electrons into separate anti-bonding orbitals with the formation of a subsequent diradical. Such a diradical might rapidly alter to a stable form either by relaxation to reform monomer, or by hydrogen atom transfer to or from a neighbouring molecule with the formation of two monoradicals. In support of such a mechanism, polymerization has been initiated by an excited triplet state of anthracene.

Alternatively it is possible that irradiation causes scission of the absorbing molecule to yield two monoradicals. The vapour phase irradiation of methylvinyl ketone has been shown to give methyl and vinyl radicals as well as carbon monoxide. A similar mechanism has been proposed for the photo-initiation of styrene, when either a styryl and a hydrogen radical, or a phenyl and a vinyl radical would be formed.

Whether the initiation mechanism leads primarily to mono- or to diradicals is still somewhat ambiguous. There is now little doubt, however, that the propagation is carried out by monoradical species.[2]

Free radicals are produced whenever liquids are exposed to a variety of ionizing radiations. The general mechanism is the same whatever the nature of the radiation.

The primary process of an interaction between ionizing radiation and a molecule is the ejection of an electron, leaving a cationic molecular species. This electron then interacts with successive molecules causing successive ionizations until its energy is dissipated. For a hydrogen-containing molecule,

$$RH + h\nu \rightarrow RH^+ + \varepsilon^\star$$
$$RH + \varepsilon^\star \rightarrow RH^+ + 2\varepsilon^\star$$

where $\varepsilon^\star$ represents a high energy electron. When these ejected electrons have expended the major portion of their energy, they can react in a variety of ways.

$$RH + \varepsilon \rightarrow RH^-$$
$$RH^+ + \varepsilon \rightarrow RH^\star$$
$$RH + \varepsilon \rightarrow RH^\star + \varepsilon$$
$$RH^+ + RH^- \rightarrow 2RH^\star$$

where $RH^\star$ represents a molecule with no excess charge, but in an excited state. The excited molecule may then decompose to free radicals or directly to molecular products. Furthermore the cation formed may also decompose to yield a free radical and a hydrogen ion,

$$RH^+ \rightarrow R\cdot + H^+$$

Neutralization of the cation by the ejected electron is an extremely rapid process, occurring in organic solvents in approximately 10^{-8} s, so that reactions initiated by ionizing radiation are generally free radical in nature. Only when the ensuing reaction of the cation is improbably rapid or when the ejected electron is immobilized, as by the presence of a solid particle, do typical cationic reactions occur.

Due to the cascade effect free radicals tend to be formed in spurs along the track of the ionizing quantum. Consequently if the radiation is characterized by high energy quanta but a low intensity of emission, the radical distribution in the liquid is not uniform, and many radicals may undergo a mutual termination reaction before diffusing to a region where they can undergo chemical reaction or polymerization. For polymerizations at high dose rates it has been found[6] that the rate of polymerization is proportional to (dose rate)$^{1/2}$, the exponent tending towards unity at lower dose rates due to the termination of radicals only in the radiation tracks.

Free radical polymerization has also been initiated during the slow neutron irradiation of alkyl halides.[7] In this case free radicals are formed by the Szilard–Chalmers mechanism.

As well as initiating normal free radical polymerization, γ-ray irradiation may also lead to the polymerization of many perfluoro monomers which do not normally polymerize by free radical mechanisms.[8] It is also possible to initiate polymerizations in the solid state or at low temperatures by the use of γ-ray irradiation. Irradiation of solid monomer or polymer leads to the formation and trapping of free radicals in the solid matrix. Upon warming or dissolution in further monomer polymerization proceeds. In this way it is possible to cross-link linear polymers, form side chains on linear polymers or to form graft co-polymers.

First Order Decomposition of an Initiator

A chemical reaction widely used as a source of free radicals is the homolytic decomposition of an organic molecule containing an unstable covalent bond. The commonest initiators are azocompounds and peroxides, although certain organometallic compounds are of increasing importance. The decomposition may be due to the thermal energy of the molecule, or may be induced by irradiation. In both cases the initial decomposition in solution is a first order process, although further radical-induced decomposition can give an order apparently greater than unity. Except in the case of organometallic compounds, the primary products of the decomposition are two free radicals.

The decomposition of peroxides is generally described as

$$ROOR' \rightarrow RO\cdot + R'O\cdot$$

and in the case of acyl or aroyl peroxides the primary radicals may lose carbon dioxide to yield the alkyl or aryl radical

$$RCO\cdot OO\ COR' \rightarrow RCOO\cdot + R'COO\cdot \rightarrow R\cdot + R' + 2CO_2$$

The initial first order homolysis is relatively insensitive to solvent,

4

although the rate of the induced decomposition depends upon the nature of the solvent. In the presence of monomer or some other radical scavengers only a negligible quantity of CO_2 is formed.

The rate of spontaneous decomposition of the peroxide is accelerated by the substitution of electron repelling groups into one or both of the benzene nuclei. It has been postulated that the two benzoyloxy groups function as dipoles linked at the negative poles. Any increase in negative charge on the peroxidic oxygen will then facilitate decomposition.

$$C_6H_5\overset{\overset{\displaystyle O}{\|}}{\underset{\delta+}{C}}-\underset{\delta-}{O}-\underset{\delta-}{O}-\overset{\overset{\displaystyle O}{\|}}{\underset{\delta+}{C}}C_6H_5$$

The rate constants k and k_0 for the decomposition of substituted and unsubstituted benzoyl peroxides respectively, can be related in terms of the Hammet equation

$$\ln (k/k_0) = \rho\sigma$$

where σ is a constant characteristic of the substituent, and ρ is a constant for the reaction involved, here homolysis. In this case Cooper[9] has evaluated ρ as -0.38.

Although many dialkyl peroxides are very unstable, tertiary peroxides have considerable stability. Di-t-butyl peroxide undergoes appreciable decomposition only at temperatures above 100°C and so is extremely safe to handle. The primary reaction products are two t-butoxy radicals. In the absence of efficient radical scavengers these radicals can undergo further decomposition to yield acetone and methyl radicals, or they can abstract hydrogen atoms from the solvent or from further peroxide to give t-butyl alcohol.

$$(CH_3)_3COO\ C(CH_3)_3 \rightarrow 2(CH_3)_3CO\cdot$$

$$(CH_3)_3CO\cdot \begin{cases} \nearrow CH_3COCH_3 + CH_3\cdot \\ \searrow_{RH} (CH_3)_3COH + R\cdot \end{cases}$$

Because of the thermal stability of this peroxide, the purely photosensitized decomposition can be studied at temperatures which would involve considerable amounts of thermal decomposition of other initiators.

The decomposition of peresters has also been used to initiate polymerization reactions, and it has been suggested[10] that fission of a C—C and the O—O bonds occurs simultaneously.

$$C_6H_5CH_2COOO\ C(CH_3)_3 \rightarrow C_6H_5CH_2\cdot + CO_2 + \cdot OC(CH_3)_3$$

Free radical polymerization has also been initiated by the decomposition of certain organo-boron peroxides.[11] The mechanism of decomposition of these compounds is not yet fully elucidated, although there is evidence to suggest that the decomposition is not wholly homolytic. Furthermore, the decomposition of peroxidized boron alkyls is accelerated by the presence of boron alkyl itself. Since the oxidation of boron alkyls and the decomposition of resulting peroxides can take place at temperatures below 0°C, boron alkyls in the presence of oxygen form convenient initiators for low temperature polymerizations.

The homolytic decomposition of organic azo compounds is a reaction widely used to initiate free radical polymerization. The most commonly used compounds are α,α'-azoaliphatic nitriles or esters. The primary decomposition process is at present believed to be simultaneous fission of both carbon to nitrogen bonds, leading to the formation of two α-cyano or α-carboxy radicals and nitrogen.

Certain organometallic compounds can undergo homolytic fission of the metal to carbon bond. One of the products is then an organic free radical capable of initiating polymerization. Thus copper and silver alkyls decompose even at low temperatures to yield alkyl radicals and the free metal.[12] These initiators are of interest both because of their usefulness at temperatures down to −70°C, and because the initiating radicals are formed singly, not in pairs. Consequently certain kinetic complications due to the recombination of primary radicals before reaction with monomer are minimized. A similar phenomenon is observed in the decomposition of phenyltitanium trialkoxides, which under the influence of ultraviolet irradiation yield phenyl radicals and relatively stable trivalent titanium compounds.[13]

The decomposition of all the initiators so far discussed can be accelerated by irradiation with light of sufficiently short wavelength. Other molecules, such as benzoin, anthracene or certain dyes, can also absorb irradiation and produce species capable of initiating free radical polymerization.

Bimolecular Initiation Reactions

Many bimolecular reactions produce free radicals, and these are frequently used to initiate polymerization. The most commonly used reactions are one-electron transfer processes which occur in certain oxidation reduction systems.

A reaction typical of this type takes place when use is made of Fenton's reagent,[14] a mixture of ferrous ions and hydrogen peroxide. One electron transfer takes place from the ferrous ion to the peroxide, yielding hydroxy radicals and a basic ferric compound.

$$HOOH + Fe^{++} \rightarrow HO\cdot + Fe^{+++}OH^-$$

In the presence of monomer the hydroxyl radicals immediately produce growing polymer chains, and induced decomposition of the hydrogen peroxide is prevented. Electron transfer can also take place from the peroxide to ferric ions, again producing free radicals.

$$Fe^{+++} + HOOH \rightarrow Fe^{++} + H^+ + \cdot OOH$$

In place of hydrogen peroxide it is possible to use a large variety of organic peroxides or hydroperoxides, as well as certain inorganic peroxides such as the persulphate ion. Similarly, many reducing agents such as inorganic cations of low valence states, hydrazine, organic amines, hydrogen sulphide or organic sulphides can replace ferrous. Although the majority of these systems have at least one water-soluble component, and are consequently of importance in emulsion polymerizations, certain are suitable for study in organic solvents. In this context systems comprising cumene hydroperoxide and ferrous complexes, or cumene hydroperoxide and amines have proved interesting.

The system ferrous acetylacetonate and cumene hydroperoxide in monomer[15] reacts to initiate polymerization much more slowly than when ferrous ion is used in aqueous solution. Furthermore, only a small percentage of the peroxide which reacts is converted to free radicals. The system cumene hydroperoxide and dimethyl aniline[16] shows similar characteristics with the added complication that the reaction is accelerated by minute traces of ferrous ion. There is also evidence in the case of dimethylaniline that the initiating radical is some nitrogen-containing species, and not the cumyloxy radical as is normally the case.

An interesting extension of these bimolecular redox systems is provided when one component is present in trace amounts, but a third substance is provided to reform the active compound. Thus only trace quantities of ferrous species are required to react with peroxides if a second reducing agent is present. Trace amounts of ferrous ion with a reducing sugar can be used in emulsion recipes, or trace quantities of ferrous or ferric compounds with benzoin can be used in organic solvents. In both cases the ferrous ions react with the peroxide to produce free radicals, and ferric compounds, the latter being reduced back to the ferrous state by the second reducing agent. In the case of the reaction between cumene hydroperoxide and small traces of ferric benzoate in the presence of benzoin in styrene as solvent, a steady state concentration of ferrous species is set up almost immediately, allowing a constant rate of initiation and illustrating the rapidity of certain oxidation–reduction reactions, even in organic solvents. The remarkable effect of traces of cupric ions in the autoxidation of many organic compounds is just one further example of the far reaching consequences of these one electron transfer processes.

Although the commonest electron transfer reactions involve peroxides, the oxidation of alcohols by ceric salts also generates free radicals.[17]

Initiation by Defect Structures

It has recently been demonstrated that ionic or free radical polymerization may be initiated by contact between monomer and freshly prepared surfaces or defect surfaces on many inorganic salts and metals.[18] In general these surfaces are prepared by subjecting a dispersion of the solid in monomer to some physical process such as agitation in a ball mill or exposure to ultrasonic vibrations.

Free radicals are also formed when polymer is subjected to these physical stresses,[19] and in this case it is assumed that the variations in mechanical forces acting on different sections of a macromolecule lead directly to fission of a covalent carbon–carbon bond.

One of the most interesting methods of initiation which has recently been examined occurs when a beam of metal atoms impinges on monomer vapour, and the combined vapours are frozen on a cold surface.[20] Not only are free radicals formed in the vapour phase, but the resulting polymer has a stereoregularity different from that formed in normal free radical polymerizations. Magnesium and mercury atoms have been used to initiate the polymerization of methyl methacrylate and acrylonitrile in this way.

Diffusion Effects in the Kinetics of Initiation

It is possible, from a study of various aspects of a polymerization reaction, to obtain a value for the rate of initiation—that is, the rate of formation of free radicals capable of propagating the polymerization chain reaction with the production of macromolecular species. This rate is often less than the rate of decomposition of the initiator (normalized by the number of radicals theoretically formed per molecule decomposed). Under these conditions the ratio of the two rates is often called the efficiency of initiation.

Initiator efficiencies less than unity can be due to two main causes. The simplest explanation is that the initiator molecule (often a species of high internal energy) can simultaneously decompose by a mechanism which does not lead to the formation of free radicals. Such a mechanism has been postulated for the decomposition of α,α'-azoisobutyronitrile and of certain organic boron peroxides.

The second main reason which has been advanced to explain low initiator efficiencies is the existence of two or more reactions which compete for the primary radical products of the initiator decomposition. Of these only an addition reaction to monomer yields free radicals counted by rate of initiation studies.

These competitive reactions are encountered irrespective of whether the primary radicals are very reactive or relatively stable. When reactive free radicals are formed in pairs, the competitive reaction is usually the mutual termination of the same two radicals. When one or more of the primary radicals is stable, the lifetime in the presence of monomer may be sufficiently great to allow reaction with another species such as a terminating agent.

The mutual termination of two reactive primary radicals formed in proximity to each other is favoured by the nature of the diffusive processes in a liquid. The best known illustration of this is the phenomenon known as the "cage effect". The initiator molecule in solution is imagined as existing on a site of a quasi-crystalline structure of the solution. It is therefore surrounded by a "shell" or "cage" of nearest neighbour solvent molecules. The decomposition of this initiator gives rise to two radicals in the same solvent shell. They may then react with each other, react with one of the cage molecules, or diffuse out of the cage and out of proximity with each other. Depending upon the relative rates of these processes the decomposition of the initiator may lead to different rates of formation of radicals which are truly free in the solution.

The kinetic consequences of cage effects are further complicated by the fact that the mutual reaction of the two primary radicals may be combination, leading to regeneration of initiator, or may be some other reaction leading to inactive products.

Denoting radicals trapped in a solvent cage by symbols in parentheses, letting $R_1 \cdot$ and $R \cdot$ represent a primary radical and a radical containing at least one monomer unit respectively, and letting Q represent the product of the reaction between two primary radicals, a reaction scheme can be devised,

1.	$Cat \rightarrow (2R_1 \cdot)$	k_1
2.	$(2R_1 \cdot) \rightarrow Q$	k_2
3.	$(2R_1 \cdot) + M \rightarrow R \cdot + R_1 \cdot$	k_3
4.	$(2R_1 \cdot) \rightleftharpoons 2R_1 \cdot$	k_D
5.	$R_1 \cdot + R_1 \cdot \rightarrow Q$	k_5
6.	$R_1 \cdot + M \rightarrow R \cdot$	k_6
7.	$R \cdot + M \rightarrow R \cdot$	k_p
8.	$R \cdot + R \cdot \rightarrow Polymer$	k_t

The caged radical may undergo either the chemical reactions 2 and 3, or the diffusive process 4. The "free" primary radicals may then undergo the termination reaction 5, or form propagating polymer chains by reaction 6. It is only reactions 3 and 6 which lead to the formation of propagating polymer chains.

The simplest treatments of reactive primary radicals assume that reaction 5 is negligible, and that once the primary radicals have diffused out of the cage they are sufficiently separated to be considered as existing at an average separation and concentration, and to exhibit an equal probability for collision with any other radical. The errors in this assumption have been examined and in particular Noyes[21] has calculated the probability that the two radicals, initially in proximity, will react with each other after a definite time. Of course if the primary radicals are not reactive towards monomer, or if the monomer concentration is very low, the probability of reaction 5 may be very large indeed. In the following treatment, however, the basic assumption will be made that once the primary radicals have diffused out of the solvent cage, they react only with monomer. As a corollary to this assumption the back diffusion of the primary radical into the cage is also ignored.

The caged pair of radicals, $(2R_1 \cdot)$ is treated as a single transient species, so that reactions 2, 3, 4, are first order in this species.

Applying the stationary state assumption to the concentration of all radical intermediates, we find

$$\frac{d[(2R_1\cdot)]}{dt} = 0 = k_1[Cat] - k_2[(2R_1\cdot)] - k_3[(2R_1\cdot)][M] - k_D[(2R_1\cdot)]$$

$$(4.1)$$

$$\frac{d[R_1\cdot]}{dt} = 0 = 2k_D[(2R_1\cdot)] + k_3[(2R_1\cdot)][M] - k_6[M][R_1\cdot] \qquad (4.2)$$

$$\frac{d[R\cdot]}{dt} = 0 = k_3[M][(2R_1\cdot)] + k_6[M][R_1\cdot] - 2k_t[R\cdot]^2 \qquad (4.3)$$

Combination of these three equations yields

$$[R\cdot] = \left\{ \frac{2k_1[Cat](k_D + k_3[M])}{2k_t(k_2 + k_D + k_3[M])} \right\}^{1/2} \qquad (4.4)$$

Whence for long chains

$$-\frac{d[M]}{dt} = \frac{k_p[M](2k_1)^{1/2}[Cat]^{1/2}}{(2k_t)^{1/2}} \left(\frac{k_D + k_3[M]}{k_2 + k_D + k_3[M]} \right)^{1/2} \qquad (4.5)$$

Depending upon whether the primary radicals escape from the cage by diffusion or by reaction with a nearest neighbour monomer molecule,

$$(a) \quad k_D \gg k_3[M], \quad -\frac{d[M]}{dt} = \frac{k_p[M](2k_1)^{1/2}[Cat]^{1/2}}{(2k_t)^{1/2}} \left(\frac{k_D}{k_2 + k_D} \right)^{1/2} \qquad (4.6)$$

$$(b) \quad k_D \ll k_3[M], \quad -\frac{d[M]}{dt} = \frac{k_p[M](2k_1)^{1/2}[Cat]^{1/2}}{(2k_t)^{1/2}} \left(\frac{k_3[M]}{k_2 + k_3[M]} \right)^{1/2} \qquad (4.7)$$

In the former case the overall rate of polymerization is first order in monomer and half order in catalyst. In the latter case the order of reaction with respect to monomer depends upon the relative magnitudes of k_2 and $k_3[M]$ being 1·5 at low monomer concentrations, falling to unity at higher concentrations if $k_3[M]$ is greater than k_2.

The efficiency of initiation predicted by this scheme depends upon whether the definition of efficiency is based upon the amount of initiator remaining at any time (as might be measured by chemical or analytical methods), or upon the total number of molecules which at some time have undergone a decomposition reaction (even though some may have been reformed by recombination of primary radicals). On the latter definition, sometimes used in connection with photosensitized decompositions, the efficiency of initiation is simply

$$f = \frac{k_D + k_3[M]}{k_2 + k_D + k_3[M]} \tag{4.8}$$

When the efficiency is based upon the amount of initiator which has disappeared from the system (the more usual definition), the nature of the reaction product Q is important. When Q is another initiator molecule, the efficiency is unity since all fragments either initiate polymerization or reform initiator. When Q is not another initiator molecule, the efficiency must be less than unity, and is, again

$$f = \frac{k_D + k_3[M]}{k_2 + k_D + k_3[M]} \tag{4.8}$$

It is interesting to note that when the "cage" recombination reforms catalyst, the rate of catalyst disappearance depends on the concentration of monomer in the system.

Bifunctional Initiation

In spite of the considerable evidence against the continued propagation of short chain diradicals, it is possible that polymeric diradicals, with the unpaired electrons separated by more monomer units than a certain critical number, might exist. Such a system can be realized by the use of a bifunctional initiator. Initiation at one functional group produces a polymeric free radical with a functional group at the other end of the chain. Decomposition of this group, after a certain critical number of propagation steps, will yield the diradical for which the probability of intramolecular termination is negligible. It is possible to devise a general kinetic scheme to cover the cases of reinitiation either before or after the termination of the radical first formed.

Experimentally such a situation has been realized[15] when polymerization is initiated by the reaction between a ferrous compound and a dihydroperoxide. The production of a chain capable of growing from each end allows information to be gathered concerning the termination process. Thus if termination occurs by way of a combination reaction, the chains will continue to grow by both the propagation and the "termination" processes until deactivated by some transfer reaction.

Many of the initiator systems mentioned in this chapter involve quite complicated reaction schemes. In these cases published work on the polymerization kinetics has been principally concerned with elucidating the initiation mechanism.

Although the detailed kinetics of these various processes differ from case to case, the algebraic manipulation of the kinetics is fairly standard, and a comprehensive coverage is not within the scope of this volume.

Some Initiation Rate Constants

When polymerization is initiated by the first order decomposition of a molecule containing a relatively unstable covalent bond, the rate constant is characterized by a high Arrhenius pre-exponential factor, and an Arrhenius activation energy which can be regarded as a measure of the bond strength.

The decomposition of benzoyl peroxide is characterized by a rate constant for which the pre-exponential factor is in excess of 10^{13} s^{-1} and the activation energy is about 30 kcal mole^{-1}. On the basis of a collision theory of reactions in liquids the pre-exponential factor of a unimolecular fission reaction is a vibration frequency. Since the vibration frequency of molecules in a liquid or of groups in a molecule is about 10^{13} s^{-1}, and since the entropy change in such a fission is usually positive, it is to be expected that on the basis of both the collision and transition state theories the experimentally determined pre-exponential factor would have a value in excess of 10^{13} s^{-1}.

The more stable di-t-butyl peroxide exhibits a frequency factor of $4 \cdot 3 \times 10^{15}$ s^{-1} and an activation energy of $37 \cdot 2$ kcal mole^{-1}.

The decomposition of azo compounds appears to be relatively insensitive to environment and the rate constant for the homolytic decomposition of α,α'-azobisisobutyronitrile has been found to have a pre-exponential factor, $1 \cdot 0 \times 10^{15}$ s^{-1} and an activation energy of $30 \cdot 5$ kcal mole^{-1}.

It can be seen that the decomposition of all these compounds exhibits the pre-exponential factor predicted by theory, and an activation energy which gives a convenient rate of decomposition at the temperature of the reaction.

The more unstable compounds used to initiate polymerization at low temperatures would be expected to have similar pre-exponential factors, but lower activation energies commensurate with the lower bond strength. In fact one of the few such compounds studied is ethylsilver. The homolytic decomposition of this compound exhibits an activation energy of 14·2 kcal mole^{-1} and a pre-exponent of 5·0 × 10^8 s^{-1}.[12] The remarkably low value of the frequency factor has been explained on the basis of a low transmission coefficient across the transition state. This low coefficient arises since undissociated ethylsilver is assumed to be predominantly ionic, whereas the products of lowest energy are the result of homolytic fission. During the reaction the fragments must convert from the ionic to the homopolar energy surfaces. The alternative explanation that the decomposition involves complexing with monomer also seems applicable in this case.

The electron transfer reaction between cumene hydroperoxide and ferrous ions in aqueous solution has a rate constant 3·9 × 10^9 exp($-11,000/RT$) 1 mole^{-1} s^{-1}.[22] Since this reaction presumably involves coordination of the peroxy group to the iron, a rather large negative entropy of activation would be expected. The low experimental Arrhenius pre-exponential factor is in line with this supposition. The related reaction between ferrous acetylacetonate and cumene hydroperoxide in hydrocarbon solvents has an overall rate constant evaluated as 10^8 exp ($-18,400/RT$) 1 mole^{-1} s^{-1}.[15] The higher activation energy for electron transfer would be predicted for a "charge-forming" reaction in media of low dielectric constant. In this case the coordination process seems to be a rapid step preceding the rate-determining electron transfer process.

REFERENCES

1. FLORY, P. J., *J. Amer. chem. Soc.*, 1937, **59**, 241.
2. JOHNSON, D. H. and TOBOLSKY, A. V., *J. Amer. chem. Soc.*, 1952, **74**, 938.
3. HAWARD, R. N., *Trans. Faraday Soc.*, 1950, **46**, 204.
4. MAYO, F. R., *J. Amer. chem. Soc.*, 1953, **75**, 6133.
5. RUSSEL, K. E., and TOBOLSKY, A. V., *J. Amer. chem. Soc.*, 1954, **76**, 395.
6. CHAPIRO, A., and WAHL, P., *C. R. Acad. Sci., Paris*, 1954, **238**, 1803.
7. MAGAT, M., *Disc. Faraday Soc.*, 1947, **2**, 284.
8. BALLANTINE, D. S., GLINES, A., COLOMBO, P. and MANOWITZ, B., U.S. Atomic Energy Comm. BNL-294 (1954).
9. COOPER, W., *J. chem. Soc.*, 1951, 3106.
10. BARTLETT, P. D., 16th Int. Congress of Pure and Applied Chemistry, Paris, 1957.
11. BAWN, C. E. H., MARGERISON, D. and RICHARDSON, N., *Proc. chem. Soc.*, 1959, 397; WELCH, F. J., *J. Polymer Sci.*, 1962, **61**, 243.
12. BAWN, C. E. H. and WHITBY, F. J., *Disc. Faraday Soc.*, 1947, **2**, 228; BAWN, C. E. H., JANES, W. H. and NORTH, A. M., *J. Polymer Sci.*, 1962, **58**, 335.
13. NORTH, A. M., *Proc. roy. Soc.*, 1960, **A254**, 408.
14. BAXENDALE, J. H., EVANS, M. G. and PARK, G. S., *Trans. Faraday Soc.*, 1946, **42**, 155.
15. BURNETT, G. M. and NORTH, A. M., *Makromol. Chem.*, 1964, **73**, 60, 67, 77.
16. MELTZER, T. H. and TOBOLSKY, A. V., *J. Amer. chem. Soc.*, 1954, **76**, 5178; IMOTO, M., OTSU, T., and OTA, T., *Makromol. Chem.*, 1955, **16**, 10.

17. MINO, G., KAIZERMAN, S. and RASMUSSEN, E., *J. Polymer Sci.*, 1959, **38**, 393.
18. KARGIN, V. A. and KABANOV, V. A., Int. Symp. Macromolecules, Moscow (1958).
19. WATSON, W. F., *Trans. Inst. Rubber Ind.*, 1953, **29**, 32; IMMERGUT, E. H. and MARK, H., *Makromol. Chem.*, 1956, **18/19**, 322.
20. KARGIN, V. A., KABANOV, V. A. and ZUBOV, V. P., *Vysokomol. Soedin.*, 1960, **2**, 303, 765.
21. NOYES, R. M., *J. Amer. chem. Soc.*, 1955, **77**, 2042; 1956, **78**, 5486.
22. FORDHAM, J. W. L. and WILLIAMS, H. L., *J. Amer. chem. Soc.*, 1951, **73**, 1634.

CHAPTER 5

RADICAL–MOLECULE REACTIONS

A. Propagation

The propagation step of polymerization is the addition of a free radical, containing at least one monomer unit, to the double bond of a monomer molecule. The reaction proceeds by interaction of the electron of unpaired spin with the π-electrons of the olefine to form a covalent bond at one carbon atom and another electron of unpaired spin at the other. In this way the product of the reaction is always a free radical containing one monomer unit more than the reacting free radical.

In the case of a vinyl monomer the newly formed covalent bond may involve the substituted carbon or the methylene group of the monomer. In the case of a free radical on the substituted carbon of the reacting species, these additions would lead respectively to "head to head" or "head to tail" propagation

$$CH_2CHX \cdot + CHX{=}CH_2 \rightarrow CH_2CHX\ CHXCH_2 \cdot$$
$$CH_2CHX \cdot + CH_2{=}CHX \rightarrow CH_2CHXCH_2CHX \cdot$$

In actual fact these two competing propagations have quite different activation energies. The "head to tail" reaction is favoured because the resulting free radical has greater resonance stabilization than a methylenic radical. Furthermore, when the substituents on the monomer molecule are bulky or polar groups, a steric or coulombic repulsion adds markedly to the free energy of the "head to head" product, and consequently to the activation energy of this particular propagation. The total difference in activation energies is such that, at temperatures normally encountered in polymerization reactions, propagation proceeds almost entirely by a "head to tail" mechanism.

Stereochemistry of Propagation

When a vinyl monomer has undergone a propagation reaction, the substituted carbon atom is attached to two methylene groups and forms part of the backbone of the polymer chain. Since in general the lengths of residual polymer chain attached to each of these methylene groups are unequal, the propagation reaction has formed an asymmetric centre. This newly formed asymmetric carbon atom can then exist in two stereoisomeric forms, which may be pictured in the Newman convention.

In illustrations of the two stereoisomers (a) and (b), the polymer chain extensions are considered in a *trans* conformation, and in the illustrations (c) and (d) the *gauche* arrangements of the same two stereoisomers are portrayed. There is evidence that certain polymers, such as polyvinyl chloride, preferentially adopt the *trans* conformations, while others, such as polystyrene, adopt a helical arrangement of gauche conformations.

In discussing the detailed microstructure of a polymer chain, it is now usual to refer to units of either two, or three, consecutive asymmetric centres.

When two centres are under consideration, the unit is termed an isotactic or a syndiotactic diad if the two asymmetric carbon atoms have the same or opposite configurations respectively. When units of three asymmetric centres are considered, the sequences *d.d.d* or *l.l.l* are termed isotactic triads, the sequences *d.l.d* or *l.d.l* are syndiotactic triads, and *l.l.d*, *l.d.d*, *d.l.l*, *d.d.l* are heterotactic triads.

Nuclear magnetic resonance measurements are usually discussed in terms of the fraction of monomer units in the various triad placements, whereas crystallinity and other properties are often discussed in terms of diad placements. If we denote the fraction of monomer units in isotactic, heterotactic and syndiotactic triads as I_t, H_t and S_t respectively, and if I_d, S_d represent the fraction in isotactic and syndiotactic diads,

$$I_t + H_t + S_t = 1$$
$$I_d + S_d = 1$$
$$I_d = I_t + \tfrac{1}{2}H_t$$
$$S_d = S_t + \tfrac{1}{2}H_t$$

If the probability of formation of an isotactic diad can be described by a single parameter, α, the probability of formation of a syndiotactic diad is $1 - \alpha$. The probabilities of forming the three triad types are then, isotactic α^2; syndiotactic $(1 - \alpha)^2$; heterotactic $2\alpha(1 - \alpha)$. The relative concentrations of each triad are given by

$$\frac{\alpha}{1 - \alpha} = \frac{H_t}{2S_t} = \left(\frac{I_t}{S_t}\right)^{1/2}$$

Since $\alpha/(1 - \alpha)$ also equals the ratio of the two concurrent reaction rate constants describing the isotactic and syndiotactic addition reactions, it is possible to evaluate k_{pi}/k_{ps} from physical measurements of H_t/S_t or I_t/S_t.

It is also possible to express these two propagation rate constants in the Arrhenius form, when

$$\frac{\alpha}{1 - \alpha} = \exp\left(-\frac{\delta\Delta H^\star}{RT}\right)\exp\left(\frac{\delta\Delta S^\star}{R}\right)$$

$\delta\Delta H^\star$ and $\delta\Delta S^\star$ are respectively the differences in the two activation energies and activation entropies.

Nuclear magnetic resonance measurements[1] made on polymers prepared at a series of temperatures suggest that in methyl methacrylate polymerization $\delta\Delta H^\star$ is about $+1$ kcal mole^{-1}, and $\delta\Delta S^\star$ is about -1 cal deg^{-1}. The small activation energy difference is in agreement with that calculated from an assessment of the various steric interactions during propagation.

Since these energy differences are rather small, predominantly syndiotactic polymer is usually formed only at low temperatures. No monomer is yet known in which free radical polymerization yields predominantly isotactic polymer.

It is important to stress that this argument holds only for free radical propagation involving free monomer and uncomplexed free radicals.

If the propagation reaction occurs on a surface, in a crystal matrix, or in a complex of some kind, the isotactic placement may well have the lower activation energy. In fact methyl methacrylate in a solid matrix involving magnesium atoms, has been polymerized by a reaction propagated by free radicals to give isotactic polymer.[2]

In the particular case of conjugated diene polymerization the possibility of 1:4 addition exists as well as the stereoisomeric forms of 1:2 addition. In the case of substituted dienes such as isoprene the complexity is further increased by the possibility of syndiotactic and isotactic 3:4 additions. Under normal conditions free radical propagation yields polymer containing a mixture of all types of addition.

Cross-linking in Diene Polymerization

In the normal propagation of diene monomers, whether conjugated or not, the primary addition reaction yields a section of a polymer molecule which has an olefinic double bond either in the polymeric main chain or in a side group. These double bonds attached to a polymer chain may themselves act as monomer and undergo an addition reaction with a propagating free radical. The result of such a propagation step will be the junction of the two polymeric chains which were attached originally to the radical and the double bond. In this way many polymer chains may become linked together into a three-dimensional network with branch points at every such addition.

A simple kinetic treatment of this cross-linking reaction has been given by Flory.[3] Let α be the degree of conversion of monomer to polymer, $[R\cdot]$ the total concentration of free radicals in the system, and k_p and k_c the rate constants for the propagation involving a double bond in monomer and in polymer respectively. The rate of formation of linear polymeric sections is

$$d\alpha/d_t = k_p[R\cdot](1-\alpha) \tag{5.1}$$

and the rate of formation of cross-links is

$$\frac{dX_c}{dt} = 2k_c[R\cdot]\alpha \tag{5.2}$$

where X_c is the concentration of cross-linked units expressed as moles of such units per mole of monomer initially present. Division of these two equations gives

$$\frac{dX_c}{d\alpha} = \frac{2k_c\alpha}{k_p(1-\alpha)} \tag{5.3}$$

which expresses the instantaneous average concentration of cross-links on a polymer chain as a function of the degree of conversion. Integration of this equation from $\alpha = 0$ to any conversion yields the total concentration of cross-links in polymer at that conversion, which can be denoted ρ,

$$\rho = \frac{X_c}{\alpha} = -2 \frac{k_c}{k_p} \left\{ 1 + \frac{1}{\alpha} \ln (1 - \alpha) \right\} \tag{5.4}$$

As polymerization proceeds, a conversion is reached when sufficient cross-linking has taken place to join all the polymeric chains into a three dimensional network extending throughout the whole of the reaction medium. At this point the system exhibits a sharp increase in viscosity, and the phenomenon is described as the "gel point". Gelation, and the corresponding formation of the infinite network usually take place over a rather small range of conversion. Kinetic analysis of the cross-linking reaction at the gel point is rather involved, but the problem can be approached either using treatments originally devised for branch chain reactions at the explosion limits, or by the use of statistical procedures.

Using statistical methods it is possible to show that the critical conversion corresponding to the "gel point" is given by

$$\bar{r}_w{}^{-1} = -2 \frac{k_c}{k_p} \left\{ 1 + \frac{1}{\alpha_c} \ln (1 - \alpha_c) \right\} \tag{5.5}$$

where $\bar{r}_w$ is the weight average chain length of the primary chains being linked and α_c is the critical conversion. It is then possible to combine measurements of α_c and $\bar{r}_w$ in order to obtain the ratio k_c/k_p.

The polymerization of butadiene has been studied using such a treatment[4] and the ratio k_c/k_p evaluated over the temperature range 40–60°C. The ratio ranges in value from 1·02 to 1·98 over this range. Combining these results with other values of the propagation rate constant gives an activation energy for the cross-linking propagation of 17 kcal mole^{-1}.

A study of the copolymerization of methyl methacrylate and ethylene glycol dimethacrylate in which the two olefinic groups might be considered to be equally reactive has been used to confirm the simple theory at low concentrations of the divinyl monomer. At higher concentrations, however, the simple treatment outlined above does not seem to be sufficient, and this has been interpreted by Walling[5] as signifying diffusion control of the cross-linking propagation. Gordon and Roe,[6] however, in an examination of the same system, suggest that cyclization reactions are the cause of departures from agreement with the simple treatment, and that the reaction is not diffusion controlled until after the gel point has been reached. Since most cross-linking additions have rate constants considerably smaller than those characterizing diffusion controlled reactions, it is unlikely that the reaction is diffusion controlled until the viscosity of the system and the size of the polymerizing species have markedly increased.

Cross-linked polymer can be obtained not only by the direct polymerization of divinyl monomers, but also by carrying out a variety of free radical reactions on linear polymers which contain olefinic groups. The presence of extra monomer is not essential for such cross-linking reactions. Thus oxidative and mechanical degradation of linear polyisoprene or of polybutadiene lead to the formation of a cross-linked product. The vulcanization of rubber is another such reaction.

Polymerization of Dienes by Alternating Intra- and Intermolecular Propagation

A rather interesting propagation mechanism exists for the polymerization of certain non-conjugated dienes. The reaction has been studied for unsymmetrical 1,6- and 1,7-dienes, and perhaps the most spectacular example is the polymerization of diallyl quaternary ammonium compounds to polymers consisting of a chain of piperidinium rings.

Propagation has been shown[7] to proceed by the addition of a free radical to one allyl group of the monomer, which then undergoes an intramolecular addition reaction with the other allyl group, forming a free radical capable of intermolecular addition with another molecule of monomer.

Initiation

Intramolecular propagation

Intermolecular propagation

Such cyclic polymerizations have also been achieved using other initiating species such as metal alkyls.

Propagation Rate Constants

The absolute values of the propagation rate constants for free radical polymerization depend on the reactivity of both the monomer and the propagating free radical. The relative importance of these contributing factors can be separated by studying the reaction of a series of monomers with the same free radical, or by studying the interaction of a variety of radicals with the one monomer. These individual characteristics are discussed in the chapter dealing with copolymerization. It is noticeable, however, that radical reactivities determined from copolymerization experiments closely parallel propagation rate coefficients.

A selection of liquid-phase propagation rate constants, together with their Arrhenius pre-exponential factors and activation energies, is listed in Table 5.1.

TABLE 5.1

Liquid Phase Propagation Rate Constants[8]

Monomer	Temp. °C	k_p l mole^{-1} s^{-1}	$A_p \times 10^{-7}$ l mole^{-1} s^{-1}	E_p kcal mole^{-1}
Isoprene (a)	60	50	12	9·8
Butadiene (b)	60	100	12	9·3
Styrene (c)	60	176	1·1	7·8
Methyl methacrylate (d)	60	734	1·0	6·3
Acrylonitrile (e)	60	1,960	—	—
Methyl acrylate (f)	60	2,090	10	7·1
Vinyl acetate (g)	60	3,700	23	7·3
N,N-Dimethylacryl-amide (h)	50	11,000	—	—
Acrylamide (i)	25	18,000	—	—

It is apparent that the propagation activation energies fall in the range 6–10 kcal mole^{-1}, and that the Arrhenius pre-exponential factors lie between 10^7 and 2×10^8. These low pre-exponential factors can be explained by transition state theory on the basis of the large entropy decreases characterizing association reactions.

As a first approximation the activated transition state of the growth process can be considered as closely resembling the final state. The entropy of activation must then be close in magnitude to the entropy of polymerization. Since this latter entropy change is about -25 to -30 e.u. mole^{-1}, the expected pre-exponential factor,

$$A = \frac{kT}{h} \exp\left(\frac{\Delta S}{R}\right),$$

would be $10^{7 \pm 1}$.

An alternative (albeit related) approach is to consider both the propagation and the reverse, depropagation, reactions. If the pre-exponential factor of the reverse step is assumed to be 10^{13}, that for the propagation reaction is

$$A_p = 10^{13} \exp\left[\frac{\Delta S - R \ln \Delta V_m}{R}\right]$$

where ΔS is the entropy of polymerization referred to the appropriate standard states, and V_m is the volume change of the reaction. The insertion of experimentally determined values for ΔS and ΔV_m then allows calculations of A_p. Again the predicted values lie between 10^6 to 10^8 l mole^{-1} s^{-1}.

Both of these calculations contain a small error since they ignore any possible entropy of activation for depropagation. This quantity, which would lead $\Delta S^\star$ to differ from ΔS, and A_d to differ from 10^{13}, would be expected to be rather small in most cases.

It is rather interesting to compare the Arrhenius pre-exponential factors obtained in free radical polymerizations with those for cationic propagation in non-solvating media. The latter values are much smaller, a phenomenon which has been ascribed to the fact that the gegen-ion inhibits rotation of the adding monomer unit.[9] Under these circumstances two rotational degrees of freedom characterizing the monomer unit in the free radical transition state are replaced by two vibrational degrees of freedom in the cationic transition state. The ratios of the relevant partition functions for styrene are

$$f(\text{rot})^2/f(\text{vib})^2 = \frac{\left(\dfrac{8\pi^2 I k T}{h^2}\right)}{\left(\dfrac{kT}{h}\right)^2 \displaystyle\prod_{i=1}^{2} \frac{1}{V_i}} \simeq 10^3,$$

where I is the moment of inertia of the styrene molecule and V_i is a vibration frequency of the monomer. The much larger entropy decrease predicted for the transition state of the cationic polymerization does seem to be in agreement with the experimental measurements of A_p for styrene.

It must not be assumed, however, that such simple calculations are completely satisfactory. Thus the free radical polymerization of methyl methacrylate is characterized by a pre-exponential factor similar to that for styrene. Yet studies of the steric restrictions between penultimate and terminal monomer units suggest that free rotation of the monomer unit in the transition state is extremely unlikely ![10]

B. Transfer Reactions

Whenever a growing polymeric free radical reacts with a molecule in a non-additive fashion, there is formed an inactive polymer molecule and some species characterized by a number of electrons of unpaired spin which differs from that in the reactant. In the case of a radical reacting with a simple organic molecule, movement of an atom or group of atoms occurs between the two to form an inactive polymer molecule and another free radical. If it happens that the resulting free radical has a reactivity similar to that of the original radical, the net result of the reaction is a change in the molecular weight of the polymer which is formed, with no diminution of the kinetic chain length. The centre of radical reactivity has merely been transferred from the polymeric species to another molecule, and the reaction is aptly referred to as a transfer step.

Alternatively if the species formed does not have sufficient reactivity to add to monomer or undergo any reaction which might lead to the formation of propagating chains, the reaction is referred to as "degradative transfer", and as such affects both the kinetic chain length and rate of reaction. Such a situation will be discussed under the section dealing with inhibition and retardation, the criterion for a normal transfer reaction being taken as the lack of any effect on the kinetic chain length.

Consider a radical undergoing a transfer reaction with a species, X, leading to the formation of an active free radical $X \cdot$, then the reaction scheme is

Initiation: $\quad\quad\quad\quad\quad\quad\quad \rightarrow R_1 \cdot \quad\quad$ Rate R_i

Propagation: $\quad\quad\quad R_r \cdot + M \rightarrow R_{r+1} \cdot \quad$ Rate constant k_p

Transfer: $\quad\quad\quad\quad R_r \cdot + X \rightarrow A_r + X \cdot \quad\quad\quad k_x$

Reinitiation by transfer radicals:

$$X \cdot + M \rightarrow R_2 \cdot \quad\quad\quad k_{p,x}$$

Termination: $\quad\quad R_r \cdot + R_s \cdot \rightarrow A_{r+s} \quad\quad\quad k_{tc}$

$$R_r \cdot + R_s \cdot \rightarrow A_r + A_s \quad\quad\quad k_{td}$$

$$R_r \cdot + X \cdot \rightarrow A_{r+1} \quad\quad\quad k_{tc,x}$$

$$R_r \cdot + X \cdot \rightarrow A_r + Y \quad\quad\quad k_{td,x}$$

$$X \cdot + X \cdot \rightarrow \text{Products} \quad\quad\quad k_{tx}$$

On the assumption that macroradical reactivity is independent of chain length and that mutual termination of $X \cdot$ radicals is unimportant for a total radical concentration, $[R \cdot]_T$,

$$\frac{d[R \cdot]_T}{dt} = R_i - k_x[R \cdot]_T[X] - 2(k_{tc} + k_{td})[R \cdot]_T^2$$

$$- (k_{tcx} + k_{tdx})[R \cdot][X \cdot] + k_{px}[M][X \cdot] \quad\quad (5.6)$$

$$\frac{d[X \cdot]}{dt} = k_x[R \cdot]_T[X] - k_{p,x}[M][X \cdot] - (k_{tc,x} + k_{tdx})[R \cdot][X \cdot] \qquad (5.7)$$

It is possible to apply the stationary state approximation to the concentration of both radical species, so that $d[X \cdot]/dt = 0$. When $k_p[M] \gg k_x[X]$, termination involving $X \cdot$ radicals may be neglected,

$$[R \cdot] = \left[\frac{R_i}{2k_{tc} + 2k_{td}}\right]^{1/2}, \qquad -\frac{d[M]}{dt} = \frac{k_p[M]R_i^{1/2}}{(2k_{tc} + 2k_{td})^{1/2}} \qquad (5.8)$$

The rate of polymerization is unchanged by the addition of a transfer agent. The degree of polymerization is given by

$$\bar{P}^{-1} = \frac{(2k_{td} + k_{tc})}{k_p^2[M]^2} R_p + \frac{k_x[X]}{k_p[M]} \qquad (5.9)$$

$$= \bar{P}_0^{-1} + C_X \frac{[X]}{[M]} \qquad (5.10)$$

where $\bar{P}_0$ is the degree of polymerization obtained using the same monomer and initiator concentrations in absence of the transfer agent. C_X is called the transfer constant of that reagent. When transfer occurs to monomer, replacing k_x by k_f.

$$\bar{P}^{-1} = \frac{k_f}{k_p} + \frac{(2k_{td} + k_{tc})}{k_p^2[M]^2} R_p \qquad (5.11)$$

The ratio k_f/k_p is referred to as the monomer transfer constant, C_M, and represents the inverse of the maximum degree of polymerization possible in a normal homogeneous polymerization.

When a transfer reaction occurs between a propagating free radical and initiator, the relationship between the degree of polymerization and rate of polymerization is interesting, since the rates of both the initiation and the transfer reactions depend on the initiator concentration. For the first order decomposition of an initiator yielding two radicals which form propagating radicals with an efficiency of initiation f,

$$R_i = 2fk_i[I], \quad R_p = \frac{k_p[M]R_i^{1/2}}{(2k_{tc} + 2k_{td})^{1/2}} \qquad (5.12)$$

and

$$[I] = \frac{(2k_{tc} + 2k_{td})R_p^2}{2fk_ik_p^2[M]^2} \qquad (5.13)$$

So that

$$\bar{P}^{-1} = \frac{k_f}{k_p} + \frac{2k_{td} + k_{tc}}{k_p^2[M]^2} R_p + \frac{k_x(2k_{tc} + 2k_{td})}{2fk_ik_p^3[M]^3} R_p^2 \qquad (5.14)$$

Consequently, a plot of inverse degree of polymerization against rate of polymerization is a second order curve, and the ratio $(k_{tc} + 2k_{td})/k_p^2$ is obtained from the limiting slope at zero rate of polymerization. Unless the termination mechanism is known, it is not possible to obtain an unambiguous value for the transfer rate constant by comparison of the coefficients of R_p and R_p^2. If these coefficients obtained from experimental plots of inverse degree of polymerization are denoted as a and b respectively

for disproportionation $$k_x = 2fk_ik_p[M]\,\frac{b}{a} \qquad (5.15)$$

and for combination $$k_x = fk_ik_p[M]\,\frac{b}{a} \qquad (5.16)$$

In the case of certain very reactive transfer agents, the transfer constant may be evaluated by measuring the relative rates of consumption of monomer and transfer compound. In such a case for long chains,

$$\frac{d[X]}{d[M]} = \frac{k_x[X]}{k_p[M]}, \quad C_X = \frac{d\ln[X]}{d\ln[M]} \qquad (5.17)$$

Use of this method necessitates quantitative analysis of the unreacted transfer agent as a function of time, or else analysis of transfer agent incorporated in polymer. The use of radioactive transfer agents facilitates this second type of measurement.

The magnitude of the transfer constant for any agent depends on its structure and on the reactivity of the free radical. Since transfer most commonly occurs as a hydrogen abstraction reaction, the transfer constant is a measure of contributions from all the hydrogen atoms of the molecule, which contributions will depend on the bond strengths of the atoms concerned. The stability of the resulting free radical will also determine the susceptibility of certain groups to a transfer reaction. Consequently, hydrogen atoms are most likely to undergo this transfer reaction when attached to highly substituted carbon atoms. There is evidence, also, that ionic contributions to the transition state of the reaction influence the transfer constant. Under these circumstances electrophilic radicals are most likely to attack nucleophilic centres, and nucleophilic free radicals are most likely to attack electrophilic centres. As an example of this, transfer to mercaptans is thought to be influenced by contributions to the transition state such as

$$R\cdot HSR' \qquad R^+H\ S{-}R' \qquad R^+H\cdot S{-}R'$$

The effects of polarity on a number of transfer reactions have been systematized by Bamford, Jenkins and Johnston.[11] These workers used the velocity coefficient of chain transfer to toluene at 60°C as an experimental measure of general radical reactivity. It was found that a polarity factor for any radical–substrate reaction could be correlated with the Hammet σ-function by the equation

$$\log k_s = \log k_T + \alpha\sigma + \beta$$

k_s and k_T are the rate constants of the transfer reactions of a radical with substrate and toluene respectively, and α, β, are constants for the substrate. Values of α and β have been listed for several transfer agents.

Inhibition and Retardation

Propagation has been discussed as the addition of a polymeric radical to a monomer molecule, and transfer as a radical molecule reaction in which addition does not take place, but merely a change in the species possessing the centre of radical reactivity. Both of these reactions yield a free radical of reactivity the same as (or very similar to) the reactivity of the original polymeric free radical. It is possible, however, that the end product of a radical molecule addition might exhibit a reactivity considerably less than that of the original propagating radical.

In the extreme case when such a reaction occurs more readily than the propagation reaction, and the species formed does not have sufficient reactivity to undergo any reaction which might lead to the formation of propagating radicals, the growth reaction is completely suppressed. This is an inhibition reaction, and the molecule concerned is an inhibitor.

The less extreme case encompasses the possibility of the radical molecule reaction occurring with significant frequency, but not to the exclusion of the propagation reaction. If the resulting species is less reactive than the propagating free radical, the overall rate of polymerization will be reduced, but not completely suppressed. In this case the molecule is referred to as a retarder. Transfer, retardation, and inhibition can thus be seen as three particular cases of radical molecule reactions differing only in the frequency of the reaction compared with propagation, and in the reactivity of the resulting free radical.

In an inhibited polymerization the inhibitor is continuously reacting with the free radicals formed by the initiation reaction. It is then possible, when less inhibitor than initiator is present at the start of the reaction, for the inhibitor to be completely consumed. The polymerization might then proceed at the same rate as would have occurred in the absence of any added substance. (This is assuming that the products of the inhibition reaction are inactive and that decrease in initiator concentration is negligible.)

When the concentration of inhibitor is so low that the propagation reaction does occur, the last traces of the compound function as a retarder. The essential characteristic of a retarder is that the rate of polymerization is never zero, but slowly builds up as retarder is consumed. Finally a maximum rate, that operative in absence of retarder, is achieved.

In the case of polymerization in which retardation and inhibition reactions take place, a precise kinetic analysis is more difficult than when simple transfer is operative. The stability of the resulting species is such that it might undergo changes in concentration making any stationary state assumption inapplicable. It is most convenient to apply the general reaction scheme set forth for transfer reactions to some specific types of retarded or inhibited polymerizations.

Kinetic Treatment of an Ideal Retarder[12]

An ideal retarder is a compound which reacts directly with growing free radicals to yield products incapable of further reaction. Then $k_{tx}[R\cdot][X\cdot]$ and $k_{px}[M][X\cdot]$ are negligible. Since the agent is a retarder and not an inhibitor, $k_p[M]$ is not negligible by comparison with $k_x[X]$. Then

$$\frac{d[R\cdot]}{dt} = R_i - k_x[R\cdot][X] - 2k_t[R\cdot]^2 \qquad (5.18)$$

and

$$-\frac{d[X]}{dt} = k_x[X][R\cdot] \qquad (5.19)$$

By obtaining [X] from equation (18), differentiating with respect to time and substituting for $d[X]/dt$ from equation (19), there results

$$-\frac{1}{k_x[R\cdot]}\left(\frac{d^2[R\cdot]}{dt^2}\right) - \frac{d[R\cdot]}{dt}\left(\frac{R_i}{k_x[R\cdot]^2} + \frac{2k_t}{k_x} + 1\right)$$

$$+ \left(\frac{d[R\cdot]}{dt}\right)^2 \frac{1}{k_x[R\cdot]^2} + R_i - 2k_t[R\cdot]^2 = 0 \quad (5.20)$$

If adjustments in the radical concentration take place over times which are very short compared with the times for changes in the retarder concentration, it is possible to apply a quasistationary state approximation to the concentration of propagating radicals, whence

$$\frac{d[R\cdot]}{dt} \ll R_i \text{ and } \frac{1}{k_x[R\cdot]^2}\left(\frac{d[R\cdot]}{dt}\right)^2 \ll \frac{R_i}{2k_t[R\cdot]^2} \times \frac{d[R\cdot]}{dt} \quad (5.21)$$

If also $k_x \ll 2k_t$ (which in practice will be the case for a retarder as opposed to an inhibitor), equation (20) reduces to

$$-\frac{d^2[R\cdot]}{dt^2} \times \frac{1}{k_x[R\cdot]} - \frac{d[R\cdot]}{dt}\left(\frac{R_i}{k_x[R\cdot]^2} + \frac{2k_t}{k_x}\right) + R_i - 2k_t[R\cdot]^2 = 0$$

$$(5.22)$$

In fact, that $k_x \ll k_t$ can be shown to follow from the assumption that the stationary state approximation is valid. By examining the maximum value of $\dfrac{d^2[R\cdot]}{dt^2} \times \dfrac{1}{k_x[R]}$ it can be shown that this term too is negligible when $d[R\cdot]/dt \ll R_i$, so that

$$-\frac{d[R\cdot]}{dt}\left(\frac{R_i}{k_x[R\cdot]^2} + \frac{2k_t}{k_x}\right) = 2k_t[R\cdot]^2 - R_i \quad (5.23)$$

$$\int \frac{(R_i + 2k_t[R\cdot]^2)\,d[R\cdot]}{[R\cdot]^2(1 - 2k_t[R\cdot]^2)} = k_x t + \text{constant} \quad (5.24)$$

or $\qquad -\dfrac{[R\cdot]_m}{[R\cdot]} + \ln\dfrac{[R\cdot]_m + [R\cdot]}{[R\cdot]_m - [R\cdot]} = k_x[R\cdot]_m t + A \quad (5.25)$

where A is a constant, $[R\cdot]$ the radical concentration at the time t, and $[R\cdot]_m$ the final maximum radical concentration when $[X]$ is zero. Introducing a reduced rate of polymerization, Φ_t, as the ratio of the rate of polymerization at time t to the final maximum rate, when $[X] = 0$

$$\Phi_t = [R\cdot]/[R\cdot]_m \quad (5.26)$$

when $\qquad \dfrac{1}{\Phi_0} - \dfrac{1}{\Phi_t} + \ln\left(\dfrac{1 - \Phi_0}{1 + \Phi_0} \times \dfrac{1 + \Phi_t}{1 - \Phi_t}\right) = k_x[R\cdot]_m t \quad (5.27)$

where Φ_0, the value of Φ_t at $t = 0$ is given by

$$\Phi_0 = (2R_i k_t)^{1/2}/k_x[X] \quad (5.28)$$

Then if $\Phi_0 \ll 1$,

$$\frac{1}{\Phi_0} - \frac{1}{\Phi_t} + \ln \frac{1 + \Phi_t}{1 - \Phi_t} = k_x[\text{R}\cdot]_m t \qquad (5.29)$$

It is possible to choose a value of Φ_t, and a corresponding value of t, such that

$$-\frac{1}{\Phi_t} + \ln \frac{1 + \Phi_t}{1 - \Phi_t} = 0$$

At this value of t, which can be called τ,

$$\frac{1}{\Phi_0} = k_x[\text{R}\cdot]_m \tau \qquad (5.30)$$

or $$\tau = [\text{X}]_0 / R_i \qquad (5.31)$$

The solution of

$$\ln \frac{1 + \Phi_t}{1 - \Phi_t} = \frac{1}{\Phi_t} \quad \text{is} \quad \Phi_t = 0{\cdot}648$$

Consequently measurement of the time when the rate of polymerization has attained a value 0·648 of the final maximum value allows computation of R_i. Furthermore, equation (25) can be written as

$$\frac{1}{\Phi_t} + \ln \frac{1 + \Phi_t}{1 - \Phi_t} = k_x[\text{R}\cdot]_m t + A \qquad (5.32)$$

and a curve of Φ_t against $k_x[\text{R}\cdot]_m t + A$ can be constructed. Comparison with the experimental curve relating Φ_t with time allows evaluation of $k_x[\text{R}\cdot] = k_x(R_i/2k_t)^{1/2}$. Since R_i has been determined, the ratio $k_x/(2k_t)^{1/2}$ or k_x/k_p can then be obtained.

Such measurements are applicable only to ideal retarders when

$$0 \neq \frac{d[\text{R}\cdot]}{dt} \ll R_i, \quad (2R_ik_t)^{1/2}/[\text{X}] \ll k_x \ll 2k_t$$

When termination occurs completely by reaction with retarder, and the rate of disappearance of this retarder can be measured

$$\frac{d[\text{X}]}{d[\text{M}]} = \frac{k_x[\text{X}][\text{R}\cdot]}{k_p[\text{M}][\text{R}\cdot]}, \quad \frac{k_x}{k_p} = \frac{d \ln [\text{X}]}{d \ln [\text{M}]} \qquad (5.33)$$

which is analogous with equation (17) for the case of transfer without retardation.

For the case of a retarded polymerization where it is not possible to measure the rate of disappearance of the retarder, and for which $k_x^2[X]^2 \gg 4k_t R_i$, termination is almost exclusively by reaction of radicals with retarder,

$$R_i = - \, \mathrm{d}[X]/\mathrm{d}t \text{ whence } [X] = [X]_0 - R_i t \qquad (5.34)$$

Since $\qquad -\mathrm{d}[M]/\mathrm{d}t = R_p = k_p[M]R_i/k_x[X] \qquad (5.35)$

$$R_p^{-1} = k_x[X]_0/R_i k_p[M] - k_x t/k_p[M] \qquad (5.36)$$

A plot of reciprocal rate of polymerization against time is then a straight line of slope $k_x/k_p[M]$ and for which

$$\text{Slope/Intercept} = R_i/[X]_0 \qquad (5.37)$$

This relationship again allows the evaluation of the rate of initiation.

In the extreme case when $k_x[X] \gg k_p[M]$, the molecule is an inhibitor, and the rate of polymerization is effectively zero until the inhibitor concentration is reduced to a negligible value. Then if t_I is the inhibition time,

$$R_i = - \, \mathrm{d}[X]/\mathrm{d}t \simeq [X]_0/t_I \qquad (5.38)$$

Depending on the magnitude of k_x (that is the reactivity of the retarding molecule), it is possible to use one of these three treatments and so obtain the rate of initiation and the ratio k_x/k_p.

It is unfortunately the case that very few retarders are ideal, in that the products often react further. In the case of certain inhibitors, such as the stable free radical diphenylpicrylhydrazyl, the initial reactant functions as an inhibitor or very reactive species, whereas the products of the reaction are much less reactive, and function merely as retarders. It is then often possible to separate the two kinetic effects resulting from inhibition followed by retardation.

The use of certain inorganic retarders, such as ferric compounds, often approximates to ideal behaviour. The ferric species react with a free radical to undergo a one-electron transfer reaction,

$$X-Fe^{+++} + R\cdot \rightarrow Fe^{++} + R^+X^-$$

Although the ferrous species which is formed might undergo an electron transfer reaction to regenerate ferric,

$$Fe^{++} + R\cdot \rightarrow Fe^{+++}R^-$$

in fact any free radical which is sufficiently nucleophilic to react with the ferric species will not be sufficiently electrophilic to undergo any appreciable reaction with the ferrous species.

In general any organic molecule retarder must function by the formation of a free radical, which although relatively stable as regards any propagation reaction, must almost certainly participate in termination reactions.

Products of the Primary Retardation Can React Further

Several complex kinetic schemes have been proposed to cover the various complications which may arise when the products of the primary retardation reaction can react further. The most general scheme is that proposed by Kice[13] which includes the termination reaction

$$\mathrm{X}\cdot + \mathrm{X}\cdot \xrightarrow{k_{t,w}} \text{Products}$$

as well as the reactions set forth in the general scheme in the section describing transfer reactions. By a kinetic analysis of this scheme of reactions the equation is obtained,

$$\frac{\Phi[\mathrm{X}]}{1-\Phi^2}\left[1+\left\{1+\frac{(1-\Phi^2)}{\phi^2\Phi^2}\right\}^{1/2}\right] = \frac{2k_t R_p}{k_p k_x}\left\{1-\frac{(1-\Phi^2)}{\phi^2\Phi^2}\right\}^{1/2}$$
$$+\frac{2k_{p,x}k_t[\mathrm{M}]}{k_{t,x}k_x} \quad (5.39)$$

where again $\Phi = R_p/R_{p,m}$ and $\phi = k_{t,x}/(2k_t)^{1/2}(2k_{t,w})^{1/2}$. R_p and $R_{p,m}$ are the rates of polymerization in the presence and absence of retarder respectively, and ϕ has the same significance as in considerations of copolymerization, being a measure of the importance of the cross-termination reaction. In order to use this equation to evaluate the rate constants it is necessary to assume a value for ϕ. The simplest procedure is to try a number of values covering a wide range, and to use the value which gives the best straight line when the left hand side of equation (39) is plotted against $R_p\left\{1+\frac{(1-\Phi^2)}{\phi^2\Phi^2}\right\}^{1/2}$. Then the slope of this straight line will be $2k_t/k_p k_x$ and the intercept $2k_{px}k_t[\mathrm{M}]/k_{tx}k_x$. From a knowledge of the values of k_t and k_p it is then possible to calculate k_x and k_{tx}. The appropriate value of ϕ can then be used to give k_{tw}.

This kinetic scheme can be applied to the case of transfer reactions with the solvent which often result in only a very slight retardation. In such cases the apparent order of the polymerization with respect to

monomer is not constant, but increases as the concentration of monomer decreases. Such a scheme can also be applied to the most commonly
used retarders such as amines, hydroquinone derivatives, nitro compounds, mercaptans, and quinones. In the last named case there is the
possibility that the propagating free radical adds to the retarders and
consequently quinone molecules become incorporated into the polymer
chain.

REFERENCES

1. Fox, T. G. and Schnecko, H., *Polymer*, 1962, **3**, 575.
2. Kargin, V. A., Kabanov, V. A. and Zubov, V. P., *Vysokomol. Soed.*, 1960, **2**, 303.
3. Flory, P. J., *J. Amer. chem. Soc.*, 1947, **69**, 2893.
4. Morton, M., Salatiello, P. P. and Landfield, H., *J. Polymer Sci.*, 1952, 8, 111.
5. Walling, C., *J. Amer. chem. Soc.*, 1945, **67**, 441.
6. Gordon, M. and Roe, R. J., *J. Polymer Sci.*, 1956, **21**, 27, 39, 57, 75.
7. Butler, G. B., Granshaw, A. and Miller, W. L., *J. Amer. chem. Soc.*, 1958, **80**, 3615.
8. (a) Morton, M., Salatiello, P. P. and Landfield, H., *J. Polymer Sci.*, 1952, 8, 279; (b) Morton, M., Salatiello, P. P. and Landfield, H., *J. Polymer Sci.*, 1952, 8, 215; (c) Matheson, M. S., Bevilacqua, E. B., Auer, E. E., and Hart, E. J., *J. Amer. chem. Soc.*, 1951, **73**, 1700; (d) Matheson, M. S., Bevilacqua, E. B., Auer, E. E. and Hart, E. J., *J. Amer. chem. Soc.*, 1949, **71**, 497; (e) Bamford, C. H., Jenkins, A. D. and Johnston, R., Unpublished work referred to in (12); Bamford, C. H., Barb, W. G., Jenkins, A. D. and Onyon, P. F., *Kinetics of Vinyl Polymerization by Radical Mechanisms*, Butterworths, London; (f) Matheson, M. S., Bevilacqua, E. B., Auer, E. E. and Hart, E. J., *J. Amer. chem. Soc.*, 1951, **73**, 5395; (g) Matheson, M. S., Bevilacqua, E. B., Auer, E. E. and Hart, E. J., *J. Amer. chem. Soc.*, 1949, **71**, 2610; (h) North, A. M. and Scallan, A. M., *Polymer*, 1964, **5**, 447; (i) Dainton, F. S. and Tordorff, M., *Trans. Faraday Soc.*, 1957, **53**, 499.
9. Kanoh, N., Higashimura, T. and Okamura, S., *Makromol. Chem.*, 1962, **56**, 65.
10. Bawn, C. E. H., Janes, W. H. and North, A. M., *J. Polymer Sci.*, 1964, **C4**, 427.
11. Bamford, C. H., Jenkins, A. D. and Johnston, R., *Trans. Faraday Soc.*, 1959, **55**, 418.
12. Bamford, C. H., Barb, W. G., Jenkins, A. D. and Onyon, P. F., *Kinetics of Vinyl Polymerization by Radical Mechanisms*, Butterworths, London (1958).
13. Kice, J. L., *J. Amer. chem. Soc.*, 1954, **76**, 6274; *J. Polymer Sci.*, 1956, **19**, 123.

CHAPTER 6

BIMOLECULAR TERMINATION REACTIONS

Chemical Aspects of the Reaction

There are two possible mechanisms whereby free radicals may react and be removed from the polymerization system in pairs.

(a) Disproportionation, in which one radical abstracts an atom from the other so as to form two polymer molecules, one of which is saturated, and the other contains a double bond. In free radical polymerization the atom transferred is usually hydrogen, and since the free radical is usually situated on the end of the growing polymer chain, the unsaturated polymer contains a terminal double bond.

(b) Combination, in which the two radicals of unpaired spin react to form a single covalent bond uniting the two original radical residues.

Several methods have been evolved in an attempt to distinguish between these mechanisms. For the main part these can be divided into three groups.

(i) Arguments by analogy with the behaviour of non-macromolecular radicals.

(ii) Analysis of certain groups in the resulting polymer.

(iii) Study of kinetic and related data such as the rate constants, rates of initiation, molecular weights of the polymer formed and other properties of the system which can be brought under observation.

Arguments by analogy are often useful guides to the mechanisms operative in macromolecular reactions, but on certain occasions may prove quite misleading and certainly cannot be regarded as unambiguous proof of mechanism.

Although the concentration of end groups in a normal polymer chain is so minute as to make normal chemical analysis difficult, it has been achieved in certain cases.

If the initiating radical contains some characteristic group, then the polymer formed by combination of two radicals will contain two such groups (one on each end of the chain), whereas the polymer formed by the disproportionation reaction will contain only one such group. Measurement of the total number of end groups in a polymer sample can be carried out by spectral analysis or by radiotracer techniques. In order to find the number of groups per molecule it is also necessary to know accurately the absolute value of the molecular weight of the polymer.

In addition to any uncertainties arising from molecular weight determinations, misleading results can be obtained due to the effect of transfer reactions. Transfer to monomer or solvent forms a polymer chain with an initiator group at one end only, simulating disproportionation, as well as forming a growing radical with no initiator group. The overall effect is then to lower the number of characteristic groups per polymer molecule. Transfer to initiator can yield polymer with a characteristic group at each end, simulating combination, and so raises the average number of initiator fragments per polymer molecule.

A related method which obviates the need for absolute molecular weight determinations is the use of initiators containing functional groups which may later be linked by some condensation reaction. On treating a polymer initiated by such a species with the condensing reagent, a molecular weight increase should be observed. In the case of polymer formed by disproportionation the molecular weight should double, and in the case of polymer formed by combination a theoretically infinite increase in the molecular weight is possible. Again this method is rigorous only in the absence of transfer reactions.

Various relationships can be derived which will allow inferences as to the nature of the termination reaction to be drawn from a study of the kinetics of the polymerization reaction.

It is possible to derive a relationship between the degree of polymerization of the polymer which is formed and the rate of polymerization in terms of the rate constants for the individual steps of the reaction. It has already been shown that for monofunctional initiation

$$\bar{P}^{-1} = \frac{k_f}{k_p} + \frac{k_{t,c} + 2k_{td}}{k_p^2[\mathrm{M}]^2} R_p \tag{6.1}$$

and for bifunctional initiation

$$\bar{P}^{-1} = \frac{k_f}{k_p} + \frac{k_{td}}{k_p^2[\mathrm{M}]^2} R_p \tag{6.2}$$

The ratio of the slopes of the plots of the inverse degree of polymerization against rate of polymerization for the two types of initiation is then equal to $2 + \beta$, where $\beta = k_{tc}/k_{td}$ represents the ratio of the number of radicals which disappear by combination to the number which disappear by disproportionation.

It is also possible to determine which mechanism is operative in the case of monoradical polymerization by combining a third kinetic observation with those commonly made, such as the rate and degree of polymerization. This is most easily achieved by measurement of the rate of initiation using some observation which does not depend on the molecular weight of the polymer formed (e.g. the rate of disappearance of some inhibitor). Then

$$\frac{R_p^2}{R_i} = \frac{k_p^2[\text{M}]^2}{2(k_{tc} + k_{td})} = \frac{k_p^2[\text{M}]^2}{2k_{td}(1 + \beta)} \tag{6.3}$$

And the slope of the plot of inverse degree of polymerization against rate of polymerization gives

$$S = \frac{k_{td}(2 + \beta)}{k_p^2[\text{M}]^2} \tag{6.4}$$

so that it is possible to calculate β as

$$\beta = \frac{2(R_p^2 S - R_i)}{R_i - 2R_p^2 S} \tag{6.5}$$

A third expression which may be used to distinguish which termination mechanism is operative can be derived from the fact that the two termination processes yield polymer of different molecular size distributions. The treatment of these distributions is set forth in a simplified form in Chapter 2, and is dealt with in greater detail in another volume[1] in this series. It is, however, relevant at this juncture to point out that the ratio of the weight average molecular weight to the number average molecular weight is given by

$$\frac{\bar{M}_w}{\bar{M}_n} = \frac{\left(\sum_{i=0}^{\infty} n_i M_i^2\right)\left(\sum_{i=0}^{\infty} n_i\right)}{\left(\sum_{i=0}^{\infty} n_i M_i\right)^2} = \begin{matrix} 2 \text{ disproportionation} \\ \text{or} \\ 1 \cdot 5 \text{ combination} \end{matrix} \tag{6.6}$$

Despite the apparent simplicity of this ratio, the complications due to transfer reactions, diffusion effects, and inaccuracies in molecular weight measurements have prevented its use as a reliable guide to the elucidation of the mechanism of the termination reaction.

The monomer most widely studied has been styrene. Radiochemical end-group analysis,[2] condensation of polymer formed with reactive end groups,[3] bifunctional initiation[4] and molecular weight–rate of initiation studies[5] all indicate that termination is predominantly by way of combination over all temperatures normally encountered in the polymerization of this monomer. Considerable attention has also been devoted to termination in methyl methacrylate polymerization. In this case the condensation of polymer containing reactive end-groups indicated that termination occurred almost entirely by disproportionation at 90°C.[3] Radiotracer analysis of the number of initiator fragments incorporated in the polymer also suggest that termination is mainly by disproportionation.[2] Bevington, Melville and Taylor[2] have evaluated the ratio k_{td}/k_{tc} for methyl methacrylate at three temperatures and find values 5·75 at 60°C, 2·13 at 25°C and 1·50 at 0°C. These values suggest that combination should be predominant at temperatures below 0°C, and that the activation energy difference between disproportionation and combination is greater than 4 kcals mole^{-1}, which seems rather large. An examination of the polymerization between −20°C and −45°C has suggested[6] that disproportionation is still important at low temperatures, but experimental inaccuracies have so far prevented an unambiguous settlement of this point.

The termination reaction in the case of acrylonitrile has been shown by two methods[3,7] to be predominantly combination, and the method of condensing reactive end groups has been used[3] to postulate that vinyl acetate undergoes termination by disproportionation at 90°C. In view of the large amount of transfer which takes place in vinyl acetate polymerization at higher temperatures, it appears that further study of this monomer is required before certain differentiation can be made.

In general it might be expected that vinylidene monomers, because of steric effects, might terminate predominantly by disproportionation, whereas vinyl monomers, unless containing a group susceptible to transfer reactions, will terminate by combination.

Physical Aspects of the Termination Reaction

In almost all early published kinetic treatments of radical polymerization reactions it is assumed either that the reactivity of the growing polymeric radical is independent of the radical degree of polymerization, or that the propagation and a factorized termination rate constant exhibit comparable variations with chain length. There are, however physical reasons why this reactivity–chain length assumption may not be valid. Such a situation has been introduced in Chapter 2 when it was pointed out that if the termination reaction is "diffusion-controlled" the overall rate of the termination reaction, and hence of the complete polymerization, will depend on the rates of diffusion of the macro-radicals, and not on their reactivity. The diffusion rates of macro-radicals will almost certainly be some function of the radical size.

In the case of reaction between two polymeric species in which the active centres are localized on a small section of the molecule, it is advantageous[8] to consider three processes before the radicals, initially "free" in solution are converted to inert polymer.

The first stage is the translational diffusion of the centres of gravity of the two reacting macroradicals to a distance such that chemical reaction is possible without alteration in the separation of centres. This is followed by the segmental diffusion of the active centres on the macromolecular chains to within the separation distance of a few angstrom units required for chemical reaction, which is the final stage of the three processes.

$$R_A \cdot + R_B \cdot \underset{k_2}{\overset{k_1}{\rightleftharpoons}} (\dot{R}_A \dot{R}_B)$$

$$(\dot{R}_A \dot{R}_B) \underset{k_4}{\overset{k_3}{\rightleftharpoons}} (R_A : R_B) \qquad \text{Overall rate}$$
$$= k_t [R_A \cdot][R_B \cdot]$$

$$(R_A : R_B) \overset{k_c}{\longrightarrow} A_{A+B} \text{ or } A_A + A_B$$

where $(\dot{R}_A \dot{R}_B)$ represents a pair of macroradicals with the centres of gravity the collision distance apart, but with the loci of reactivity on each chain separated by a distance too great to allow chemical reaction. $(R_A : R_B)$ represents the collision pair of macroradicals with the active centres sufficiently close for chemical reaction.

The assumption of a stationary state concentration of all the intermediate species, yields

$$k_t = \frac{k_1 k_3}{k_2 k_4} \left[\frac{k_4 k_c}{k_4 + k_c} \middle/ \left\{ 1 + \frac{k_3}{k_2} \left(\frac{k_c}{k_4 + k_c} \right) \right\} \right] \qquad (6.7)$$

In the case of a chemical reaction which is very much slower than either diffusive process, $k_c \ll k_4$, $k_c \ll k_4 k_2 / k_3$ and

$$k_t = \frac{k_1 k_3}{k_2 k_4} \times k_c \qquad (6.8)$$

In the virtual absence of chemical reaction the overall rate constant possesses the form which is simply an elaboration of that for any reaction in solution derived in Chapter 2 and is merely the product of an equilibrium constant governing the formation of reactive pairs and a chemical rate constant for the reaction occurring in these pairs.

If the chemical reaction is very much more rapid than segmental diffusion of the active sites on the polymeric radical ($k_c \gg k_4$), the reaction, now diffusion controlled has the overall rate constant

$$k_t = \frac{k_1 k_3}{k_2 + k_3} \tag{6.9}$$

The dependence of the diffusion-controlled rate constant upon such physical parameters as solution viscosity and radical chain length can be obtained in an approximate form[9] by the use of the Smoluchowski equation.

When translational diffusion of the macroradical is the rate-determining step of the process,

$$k_t = k_1 = 4\pi R_{AB}(D_A + D_B) \tag{6.10}$$

where D_A, D_B are the translational self-diffusion coefficients of polymeric reactants A and B respectively, and R_{AB} is the distance between the centres of gravity of the two reactants at which reaction is possible.

This encounter separation R_{AB} can be described by a random-walk expression (since we are dealing with flexible chains)

$$R_{AB}^2 = R_A^2 + R_B^2 \tag{6.11}$$

If the diffusion coefficient obeys an Einstein–Stoke's relationship,

$$D_A = kT/B\eta R_A \tag{6.12}$$

where B is a constant which is 6 for large particles, then

$$k_1 = \frac{4kT}{B\eta}\left\{\left(1 + \frac{R_A^2}{R_B^2}\right)^{1/2} + \left(1 + \frac{R_B^2}{R_A^2}\right)^{1/2}\right\} \tag{6.13}$$

Substituting the proportionality, $R_A \propto N_A^{1/2}$ where N_A is the chain length of reactant A,

$$k_1 = \frac{4kT}{B\eta}\left\{\left(1 + \frac{N_A}{N_B}\right)^{1/2} + \left(1 + \frac{N_B}{N_A}\right)^{1/2}\right\} \tag{6.14}$$

The chain length dependence of this rate constant is small, and is a minimum (independent of molecular size) in monodisperse systems.

The formulation of an overall rate constant for the situation when the rearrangement process is rate-determining is hindered by the necessity of formulating a quantitative model for the segmental motion of polymer chains in solution. In order to avoid this difficulty a simplified model has been envisaged in which the encounter dimensions are characteristic of the active chain end, but the rate of diffusion is reduced to the rate of translational diffusion of the whole macromolecule.

Under these circumstances

$$k_t = 4\pi P_{AB} R_E (D_A + D_B) \qquad (6.15)$$

where R_E is the distance between the active centres at termination and P_{AB} is a steric factor to take into account the fact that diffusion together of the active chains is inhibited by the excluded volume of the chains. Then

$$k_t = \frac{4kT P_{AB} R_E}{B\eta x_0} (N_A^{-1/2} + N_B^{-1/2}) \qquad (6.16)$$

where $x_0 = R_A/N_A^{1/2} = R_B/N_B^{1/2}$.

The chain length dependence of this rate constant is quite large, predicting that the rate of termination of a radical, chain length 10^2, is more than five times greater with a radical of unit chain length than with one of the same chain length. Such behaviour has been observed in the low temperature polymerization of methyl methacrylate.[6]

Various other models for approximating the segmental diffusion of the reacting macroradicals have been examined, and in every case the dependence on chain length is less than that expressed in equation (16).

The Kinetics of Polymerization with Diffusion-controlled Termination

The overall kinetics of polymerization for systems in which the termination reaction is diffusion-controlled have been investigated by Benson and North.[9] The method used is essentially an extension of that due to Herrington and Robertson,[10] and is an interesting example of the way one can derive kinetic relationships and size distributions for fairly complicated polymerization systems.

For purposes of simplicity consider a free radical polymerization in which transfer reactions are unimportant. If k_{trs} represents the termination rate constant for radicals of size r with radicals of size s,

$$R_i = \sum_{r,s} k_{trs} P_r P_s = P^2 \sum_{r,s} k_{trs} X_r X_s \qquad (6.17)$$

where $P = \sum_m P_m$ is the total radical concentration, and $X_m = P_m/P$ is the mole fraction of radicals of length m. For the individual radical concentrations,

$$P_1 = X_1 P = \frac{R_i}{k_p M + P \sum_m k_{t1m} X_m}$$

$$X_n = X_{n-1} \left(1 + \frac{P}{k_p M} \sum_m k_{tmn} X_m\right)^{-1} \tag{6.18}$$

Defining a mean kinetic chain length, ν, as the number of monomer units polymerized per radical formed,

$$\nu = \frac{R_p}{R_i} = \frac{k_p M P}{P^2 \sum_{n,m} k_{tnm} X_n X_m} \tag{6.19}$$

This definition of ν can be used to simplify the expressions for the mole fractions of the radicals,

$$X_1 = \frac{1}{\nu} \left[1 + \frac{P^2}{R_p} \sum_m k_{t1m} X_m\right]^{-1} \tag{6.20}$$

$$X_s = \frac{1}{\nu} \prod_{n=1}^{s} \left[1 + \frac{P^2}{R_p} \sum_m k_{tnm} X_m\right]^{-1} \tag{6.21}$$

Substituting for P^2 from equation (17)

$$X_1 = \frac{1}{\nu} \left[1 + \sum_m k_{t1m} X_m / \nu \sum_{n,m} k_{tnm} X_n X_m\right]^{-1} \tag{6.22}$$

$$X_s = \frac{1}{\nu} \prod_{n=1}^{s} \left[1 + \sum_m k_{tnm} X_m / \nu \sum_{m,n} k_{tnm} X_n X_m\right]^{-1} \tag{6.23}$$

Now defining a dimensionless parameter, f_{nm}, which will express the chain length dependence of the termination rate constants,

$$f_{nm} = k_{tnm}/k_{t11} \tag{6.24}$$

allows us to introduce the auxiliary quantities f_n and F

$$f_n = f_{nm} X_m$$
$$F = f_n X_n \tag{6.25}$$

Equations (22) and (23) now become

$$\ln (X_1 \nu) = - \ln (1 + f_1/\nu F) \tag{6.26}$$

$$\ln (X_s \nu) = - \sum_{n=1}^{s} \ln (1 + f_n/\nu F) \tag{6.27}$$

When the chain length is large, $f_n \ll F$, so that it is possible to expand the logarithms, consider only the first terms in the series, and obtain the size distribution function

$$\ln (X_s \nu) = - \sum_{n=1}^{s} f_n/\nu F = - \phi_s/\nu F \tag{6.28}$$

where $\phi_s = \sum\limits_{n=1}^{s} f_n$.

Although the set of equations, (28), can be solved for the mole fractions X_s, if the functions f_{nm} are known, the solution is difficult. A simpler process is to use the normalization condition $\sum\limits_{s} X_s = 1$, when

$$\nu = \sum_{s} \exp (-\phi_s/\nu F) \tag{6.29}$$

Replacing summation by integration (for long chains).

$$\nu = \int_0^{\infty} \exp (-\phi_s/\nu F) \, ds \tag{6.30}$$

This last equation defines an algebraic relation between the quantities ν and F which, once known, completes the solution of the problem. The kinetic parameters of interest can all be expressed in terms of ν and F, so that complete solution is possible once the form of f_{nm} is known. The general solutions in terms of F are

$$P = R_i^{1/2}/k_{t11}^{1/2} F^{1/2} \tag{6.31}$$

$$R_p = k_p M R_i^{1/2}/k_{t11}^{1/2} F^{1/2} \tag{6.32}$$

$$\nu = k_p M / R_i^{1/2} k_{t11}^{1/2} F^{1/2} \tag{6.33}$$

When the rearrangement process is rate-determining, the overall rate varies as somewhat less than half order in R_i (since F is a function of R_i) and rather more than first order in monomer. When there is a large amount of transfer to monomer, the kinetic orders with respect to monomer and initiator are normal (first order and half order respectively).

The free radical polymerization of several monomers show departures from the conventional kinetic orders which could be explained by equation (32). These cases cannot be used as proof of the validity of this equation, however, since similar kinetic effects can be caused by quite different phenomena such as termination by primary radicals from the initiator or degradative transfer to solvent.

Termination by Primary Radicals

When an initiation process yields a radical different from the propagating free radicals, this primary radical can

(a) react with monomer to form a propagating radical,
(b) undergo some termination reaction with another primary radical formed in close proximity (usually from the same parent initiator molecule), or
(c) survive for a sufficient time that there is a finite probability of it terminating a growing chain.

An extension to condition (c) exists when it may undergo a termination reaction with another primary radical which was not formed during the same initiation act.

When reaction (c) occurs to an appreciable extent in a polymerization reaction, it is known as termination by primary radicals.

This primary radical reaction is generally unimportant, since the rate of addition to monomer is a very rapid process. However, if the rate of radical formation is very large, or if the monomer concentration (or the rate constant for addition to monomer) is very low these effects can be important. A numerical examination of these conditions has been carried out by Allen and Patrick,[11] and while they are all interrelated, critical values might be

$$R_i, \text{ critical} \qquad 10^{-7} \text{ mole } l^{-1} s^{-1}$$
$$[M] \text{ critical} \qquad 1 \cdot 0 \text{ mole } l^{-1}$$
$$k_{\text{add}} \text{ critical} \qquad 0 \cdot 5 \text{ l mole}^{-1} s^{-1}$$

The general kinetic effect of this phenomenon is to cause the rate of polymerization to vary as the rate of initiation raised to a power less than 0·5 (since at large R_i the extra radicals are "wasted" in termination processes) and to depend on the monomer raised to a power greater than one (since the monomer participates in the effective initiation process as well as in propagation). The general effect is thus seen to be very similar to that caused by reaction (b) discussed under cage effects in initiation.

Several kinetic discussions of effects due to primary radicals (when these were derived from initiation and transfer reactions) have been published. The most general kinetic treatment is that due to Manabe, Utsumi and Okamura,[12] who derived the radical size distribution and the relationship between the rate and degree of polymerization. The treatment presented below follows their derivation rather closely, except that we shall be interested in number average degrees of polymerization, rather than the viscosity averages discussed in the original publication.

Consider the following basic reactions.

Formation of primary
    radicals: $\qquad\qquad\qquad$ $I \to R_1\cdot$ $\qquad\qquad$ Rate $V_R = k_i I$

Initiation: $\qquad\qquad$ $R_i\cdot + M \to P_1\cdot$ $\qquad\quad$ Rate $= \sum_i k'_{pi}[R_i\cdot][M]$

Propagation: $\qquad\quad$ $P_n\cdot + M \to P_{n+1}\cdot$ $\qquad$ Rate $V = k_p[P\cdot][M]$

Transfer: $\qquad\qquad$ $P_n\cdot + M \to P_n + R_2\cdot$ $\quad$ Rate $= k_{trM}[P\cdot][M]$

$\qquad\qquad\qquad\quad$ $P_n\cdot + S \to P_n + R_3\cdot$ $\qquad$ Rate $= k_{trs}[P\cdot][S]$

$\qquad\qquad\qquad\quad$ $P_n\cdot + I \to P_n + R_4\cdot$ $\qquad$ Rate $= k_{trI}[P\cdot][I]$

Termination: $\qquad$ $P_n\cdot + P_m\cdot \to P_{n+m}$ $\qquad$ $k_{tc}[P\cdot]^2$

$\qquad\qquad\qquad\quad$ $P_n\cdot + P_m\cdot \to P_n + P_m$ $\quad$ $k_{td}[P\cdot]^2$

$$k_t = k_{tc} + k_{td}$$

$\qquad\quad$ $P_n\cdot + R_i\cdot \to P_n$ $\qquad\qquad$ Rate $= \sum_i k'_{tii}[R_i\cdot][P\cdot]$

$\qquad\quad$ $R_i\cdot + R_j\cdot \to$ Products $\qquad$ Rate $= \sum_i \sum_j k''_{tij}[R_i\cdot][R_j\cdot]$

where M is monomer, S is solvent, I is initiator, $P_n\cdot$ the growing chain of n monomer units, P_n dead polymer, $R_i\cdot$ the primary radical of form $R_1\cdot$, $R_2\cdot$ etc., and $[P\cdot]$ is the total growing chain concentration $\sum_n [P_n\cdot]$.

Assuming a stationary state concentration of growing chains of every size, it is possible to write a series of equations

$$0 = \frac{d[P_1\cdot]}{dt} = \sum_i k'_{pi}[R_i\cdot][M] - k_p[P_1\cdot][M] - k_{trm}[P_1\cdot][M]$$

$$- k_{trs}[P_1\cdot][S] - k_{trI}[P_1\cdot][I] - 2k_t[P_1\cdot][P] - \sum_i k'_{ti}[R_i\cdot][M] \quad (6.34)$$

$$0 = \frac{d[P_n\cdot]}{dt} = k_p[P_{n-1}\cdot][M] - k_p[P_n\cdot][M] - k_{trm}[P_n\cdot][M]$$

$$- k_{trs}[P_n\cdot][S] - k_{trI}[P_n\cdot][I] - 2k_t[P_n\cdot][P\cdot] - \sum_i k'_{ti}[R_i\cdot][P_n\cdot] \quad (6.35)$$

So

$$[P_n{}^\cdot] = \frac{\sum_i k'_{pi}[R_i{}^\cdot]}{k_p} \left(\frac{k_p[M]}{\substack{k_p[M] + k_{trM}[M] + k_{trs}[S] + k_{trI}[I] + 2k_t[P^\cdot] \\ + \sum_i k'_{ti}[R_i{}^\cdot]}} \right)$$

(6.36)

The stationary state concentration of all growing chains yields

$$\sum_i k'_{pi}[R_i{}^\cdot][M] = k_{trM}[P^\cdot][M] + k_{trs}[P^\cdot][S] + k_{trI}[P^\cdot][I]$$
$$+ 2k_t[P^\cdot]^2 + \sum_i k'_{ti}[R_i][M^\cdot] \quad (6.37)$$

Combining equations (36) and (37) we obtain

$$[P_n{}^\cdot] = \frac{\sum_i k_{pi}[R_i{}^\cdot]}{k_p} \left(1 + \frac{\sum_i k'_{pi}[R_i{}^\cdot]}{k_p[P^\cdot]} \right)^{-n}$$

(6.38)

Now the rate of polymer (of size n) formation is given by

$$\frac{d[P_n]}{dt} = k_{trM}[P_n{}^\cdot][M] + k_{trs}[P_n{}^\cdot][S] + k_{trI}[P_n{}^\cdot][I]$$
$$+ k_{tc} \sum_{i=1}^{n-1} [P_r{}^\cdot][P_{r-1}{}^\cdot] + k_{td}[P_r{}^\cdot][P^\cdot] + \sum_i k'_{ti}[R_i{}^\cdot][P_n{}^\cdot] \quad (6.39)$$

$$= \frac{\sum_i k'_{pi}[R_i{}^\cdot]}{k_p} \left(1 + \frac{\sum_i k'_{pi}[R_i{}^\cdot]}{k_p[P^\cdot]} \right)^{-n} \left(k_{trM}[M] + k_{trs}[S] + k_{trI}[I] \right.$$
$$\left. + k_{td}[P^\cdot] + \sum_i k'_{ti}[R_i{}^\cdot] - \frac{k_{tc} \sum_i k'_{pi}[R_i{}^\cdot]}{k_p} \right)$$
$$+ nk_{tc} \left(\frac{\sum_i k'_{pi}[R_i{}^\cdot]}{k_p} \right)^2 \left(1 + \frac{\sum_i k'_{pi}[R_i{}^\cdot]}{k_p[P^\cdot]} \right)^{-n} \quad (6.40)$$

Using the approximation

$$\sum_i k'_{pi}[R_i{}^\cdot]/k_p[P^\cdot] \ll 1$$

(6.41)

it is possible to combine equations (37) and (40) so as to obtain a series of equations of which the general form is

$$\sum_{n=1}^{\infty} n^{1+\alpha} \frac{d[P_n]}{dt} = \Gamma(2 + \alpha) \left(\frac{k_p[P\cdot]}{\sum_i k'_{pi}[R_i\cdot]} \right)^{\alpha} \times$$

$$\left(k_p[P\cdot][M] + \alpha k_{tc}[P\cdot]^2 \frac{k_p[P\cdot]}{\sum_i k'_{pi}[R_i\cdot]} \right) + \ldots \quad (6.42)$$

where α is an integer $-1, 0, 1, 2 \ldots$ and $\Gamma(x)$ is the gamma function of x.

Equation (42) yields the number and weight average degrees of polymerization as

$$\bar{P}_n = \sum_{n=1}^{\infty} n \frac{d[P_n]}{dt} \Big/ \sum_{n=1}^{\infty} \frac{d[P_n]}{dt} \quad (6.43)$$

$$= \frac{k_p[P\cdot][M] + \sum_i k'_{pi}[R_i\cdot][M]}{\sum_i k'_{pi}[R_i\cdot][M] - k_{tc}[P\cdot]^2} \quad (6.44)$$

$$\bar{P}_w = \frac{\sum_{n=1}^{\infty} n^2 \frac{d[P_n]}{dt}}{\sum_{n=1}^{\infty} n \frac{d[P_n]}{dt}} \quad (6.45)$$

$$= \frac{2k_p[P\cdot]}{\sum_i k'_{pi}[R_i\cdot]} \left\{ 1 + \frac{k_{tc}[P\cdot]^2}{\sum_i k'_{pi}[R_i\cdot][M]} \left(1 + \frac{\sum_i k'_{pi}[R_i\cdot]}{k_p[P\cdot]} \right) \right\} + 1 \quad (6.46)$$

If monomer disappears principally by the propagation reaction,

$$V = k_p[P\cdot][M] \quad (6.47)$$

and

$$[P\cdot] = \frac{V}{k_p[M]}$$

The ratio $\dfrac{\sum_i [R_i\cdot]}{[P\cdot]}$ has been found by numerical evaluation to satisfy the form

$$\frac{\sum_i [R_i\cdot]}{[P\cdot]} = \frac{k_{trM}}{k'_{pi}} + \frac{k_{trs}[S]}{k'_{pi}[M]} + \frac{k_{trI}[I]}{k'_{pi}[M]} + \frac{(2k_t)^{1/2} V_R^{1/2}}{k'_{pi}[M]} + \ldots \quad (6.48)$$

when transfer reactions are more important than primary radical termination. When transfer reactions are unimportant,

$$\frac{\sum\limits_i [R_i \cdot]}{[P\cdot]} = K[M]^{-n} \tag{6.49}$$

where K and n are functions of k_p', k_t and V_R, for which numerical solutions have been obtained.

Equations (47) and (49) can then be substituted in equation (44) to yield (for only one type of primary radical)

$$\bar{P}_n = \frac{k_p[M] + k_{pi}'K[M]^{1-n}}{k_{pi}'K[M]^{1-n} - \dfrac{k_{tc}V}{k_p[M]}} \tag{6.50}$$

It must be noted that when termination by primary radicals is excessive, it is not valid to write

$$V = \frac{k_p[M]k_i^{1/2}[I]^{1/2}}{(2k_t)^{1/2}} \tag{6.51}$$

Bamford, Jenkins and Johnston[13] have obtained formal solutions for the rate of polymerization using the approximation

$$\frac{k_{tij}''}{k_{ti}'} = \frac{k_{ti}'}{k_t} \tag{6.52}$$

This geometric mean approximation is incorrect if any (or all) of these termination reactions is diffusion-controlled. Since it now appears probable that very many radical–radical reactions are diffusion-controlled in liquid systems, a general formal solution has still to be achieved.

Termination Rate Constants

Published values for the termination rate constants for most monomers (under normal liquid-phase conditions) are remarkably similar, lying between 10^6 and 10^8 l mole^{-1} s^{-1}. Termination rate constants for some common monomers are[14]

vinyl acetate 25°C	$5{\cdot}9 \times 10^7$ l mole^{-1} s^{-1}
methyl methacrylate 30°C	$1{\cdot}7 \times 10^7$
styrene 25°C	$3{\cdot}0 \times 10^6$
acrylamide 25°C	$1{\cdot}5 \times 10^7$

Many of these measured rate constants exhibit an Arrhenius activation energy of 3 kcals mole^{-1} or less. This value is very close to the activation energy for solvent diffusion, which is the minimum possible value for a simple bimolecular process, so that it appears that many of these processes might be diffusion-controlled.

That this is indeed the case for certain monomers has been shown[8,15] by examining the dependence of k_t upon solvent viscosity, Fig. 6.1.

The termination reactions in the solution polymerization of methyl methacrylate, other alkyl methacrylates, and vinyl acetate, are all

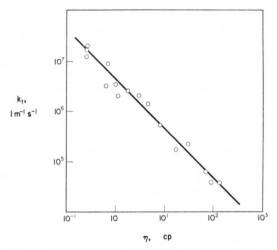

FIG. 6.1. The dependence of k_t on solvent viscosity. Polymerization of methyl methacrylate at 40°C.[8]

viscosity dependent down to the lowest attainable viscosities. The only possible interpretation of this is that these reactions are diffusion-controlled under all experimental conditions. This is rather important, because prior to 1958 it had been assumed that these reactions were not diffusion-controlled under normal solution conditions, but only became so when the presence of polymer in the system raised the viscosity to a certain critical level.

A detailed examination of the termination reaction during the initial stages of methyl methacrylate polymerization has shown that in fact the diffusion-controlled termination rate constant increases slightly with increasing conversion, before undergoing a catastrophic decrease when the viscosity of the system increases markedly. This has been explained[15] in terms of the effect of polymer concentration on the dimensions of the coiled macroradicals in solution. In dilute solutions these coils shrink with increasing concentration, and this apparently facilitates the rearrangement diffusion process. This behaviour can be described quantitatively by a virial expansion in polymer concentration, the rate constant containing a term very closely related to the second virial coefficient for the polymer solvent system. At very low conversions the rate constant exhibits a balance between this positive effect and the retarding viscous effect, and can be described by

$$k_t = k_{t,0}(1 + Ac - [\eta]c)$$

where A is a thermodynamic parameter derived from the second virial coefficient and $[\eta]$ is the intrinsic viscosity. In very good solvents $A > [\eta]$ and k_t first increases, then decreases as higher powers in the expression relating viscosity and concentration become predominant. In poor solvents $A < [\eta]$ and no such increase is observed.

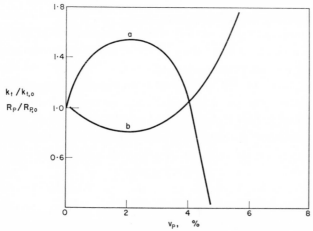

Fig. 6.2. Variation of k_t and R_p with conversion. Bulk polymerization of methyl methacrylate at 30°C. Terminating radicals degree of polymerization $1\cdot8 \times 10^4$.[15]

(a) $k_t/k_{t,0}$ (b) $R_p/R_{p,0}$.

The effects of conversion on k_t and on the overall rate of polymerization (the well-known gel effect) are illustrated in Fig. 6.2.

It is worthy of note that equations attempting to relate the value of k_t during the gel effect to the macroscopic viscosity of the polymer–non-viscous solvent system at any conversion are usually inapplicable. The main reason for this is that the viscous resistance to molecular motion in polymeric gels is not readily obtained from the macroscopic viscosity, which is predominantly caused by chain tangling phenomena. It is universally observed (in physical diffusion measurements as well as in kinetic studies) that the macroscopic observation overestimates the diffusion friction coefficient! As can be seen from Fig. 6.1, however, an Einstein–Stokes relationship does seem to hold when studies are carried out at negligible polymer concentration in inherently viscous solvents!

The effect of low temperatures on termination rate constants is particularly interesting. If the rate-determining step of the termination reaction involves motion of the polymer chain backbone, a critical temperature should exist below which this motion (a segmental rotation) cannot take place, and k_t should be markedly reduced. Just such a marked reduction (by several powers of ten) has been observed[6] for termination involving large polymethyl methacrylate radicals, although the termination reaction rate constant for small radicals are as expected by extrapolation from higher temperatures. The behaviour of the large radicals has been interpreted as a "glass transition" in the isolated dissolved macroradical occurring at approximately $-50°C$.

A final comment on the values of termination rate constants is that when values for macromolecular diffusion coefficients and dimensions are inserted into the Smoluchowski-type equations mentioned earlier in this chapter, the calculated diffusion-controlled termination rate constants have values close to $10^{-7} \, l \, mole^{-1} \, s^{-1}$, so that the evidence for the importance of diffusion in these reactions seems quite incontrovertible.

REFERENCES

1. BAMFORD, C. H. and EASTMOND, G. C., *Molecular Weight and Molecular Weight Distribution*, Pergamon, Oxford, in preparation.
2. BEVINGTON, J. C., MELVILLE, H. W. and TAYLOR, R. P., *J. Polymer Sci.*, 1954, **12**, 449.
3. BAMFORD, C. H. and JENKINS, A. D., *Nature, Lond.*, 1955, **176**, 78.
4. BURNETT, G. M. and NORTH, A. M., *Makromol Chem.*, 1964, **73**, 77.
5. MAYO, F. R., GREGG, R. A. and MATHESON, M. S., *J. Amer. chem. Soc.*, 1951, **73**, 1691.
6. HUGHES, J. and NORTH, A. M., *Trans. Faraday Soc.*, 1964, **60**, 960.
7. BAMFORD, C. H., JENKINS, A. D. and JOHNSTON, R., *Trans. Faraday Soc.*, 1959, **55**, 179.
8. BENSON, S. W. and NORTH, A. M., *J. Amer. chem. Soc.*, 1959, **81**, 1339.
9. BENSON, S. W. and NORTH, A. M., *J. Amer. chem. Soc.*, 1962, **84**, 935.
10. HERRINGTON, E. F. G. and ROBERTSON, A., *Trans. Faraday Soc.*, 1944, **40**, 236.
11. ALLEN, P. E. M. and PATRICK, C. R., *Makromol Chem.*, 1961, **47**, 154.
12. MANABE, T., UTSUMI, T. and OKAMURA, S., *J. Polymer Sci.*, 1962, **58**, 121.
13. BAMFORD, C. H., JENKINS, A. D. and JOHNSTON, R., *Trans. Faraday Soc.*, 1959, **55**, 168.
14. BAMFORD, C. H., BARB, W. G., JENKINS, A. D. and ONYON, P. F., *The Kinetics of Vinyl Polymerization by Radical Mechanisms*, Butterworths (1958).
15. NORTH, A. M. and REED, G. A., *Trans. Faraday Soc.*, 1961, **57**, 859.

CHAPTER 7

COPOLYMERIZATION

COPOLYMERIZATION is the phenomenon in which more than one type of monomer unit enter the same polymer chain. The kinetics of free radical copolymerization are of considerable importance because they afford information on the reactivities of a variety of radicals towards a single monomer, or on the relative reactivities of a series of monomers towards a reference radical. In this way it is possible to obtain information on the separate reactivities of a monomer and its derived radical, a separation which cannot be achieved from studies of the homopropagation process.

The Copolymer Composition

It is possible to derive a kinetic expression which will relate the composition of the resulting copolymer to the monomer feed composition in terms of the rate constants for the possible propagation steps.

Let us first consider the formation of a binary copolymer in which the reactivity of the growing chain is determined solely by the nature of the terminal unit containing the electron of unpaired spin. If two monomers be designated A and B, and two possible growing chains are A· and B·, the four possible propagation reactions are

$$A\cdot + A \longrightarrow A\cdot \qquad k_{pAA}$$
$$A\cdot + B \longrightarrow B\cdot \qquad k_{pAB}$$
$$B\cdot + B \longrightarrow B\cdot \qquad k_{pBB}$$
$$B\cdot + A \longrightarrow A\cdot \qquad k_{pBA}$$

For the formation of high molecular weight polymer, monomer disappears principally by the propagation reactions and

$$-\frac{d[A]}{dt} = kp_{AA}[A\cdot][A] + k_{pBA}[B\cdot][A] \qquad (7.1)$$

$$-\frac{d[B]}{dt} = k_{pAB}[A\cdot][B] + k_{pBB}[B\cdot][B] \qquad (7.2)$$

Let r be the mole ratio of A units to B units in the copolymer. Then

$$r = \frac{d[A]}{d[B]} = \frac{[A]}{[B]} \frac{k_{pAA}[A\cdot] + k_{pBA}[B\cdot]}{k_{pAB}[A\cdot] + k_{pBB}[B\cdot]} \tag{7.3}$$

The assumption of a stationary state concentration of both types of radical automatically implies that the concentration of one cannot grow at the expense of the other.

So
$$k_{pAB}[A\cdot][B] = k_{pBA}[B\cdot][A] \tag{7.4}$$

or
$$\frac{[B\cdot]}{[A\cdot]} = \frac{k_{pAB}[B]}{k_{pBA}[A]} \tag{7.5}$$

Substituting in equation (3) yields

$$r = \frac{[A]}{[B]} \times \frac{r_1[A] + [B]}{r_2[B] + [A]} \tag{7.6}$$

where $r_1 = k_{pAA}/k_{pAB}$ and $r_2 = k_{pBB}/k_{pBA}$ are known as the "reactivity ratios" of monomers A and B respectively. The reactivity ratio of any monomer is a direct measure of the relative probabilities that a radical will add to a monomer of its own, or different, type.

Equation (6), known as the "copolymer composition equation", gives the composition of the copolymer being formed at any instant during the polymerization. If the two monomers are polymerizing at different rates, the monomer composition changes with time. In order to obtain the composition of a polymer sample prepared over a time sufficiently long for such a change to take place, it is necessary to integrate equation (3).

The integrated equation yields[1]

$$\ln([A]/[B]) = \frac{r_1}{1 - r_1} \ln \frac{[A][B]_0}{[A]_0[B]} - \frac{1 - r_1 r_2}{(1 - r_1)(1 - r_2)}$$
$$\left\{ \ln \frac{(r_2 - 1)[B]/[A] - r_1 + 1}{(r_2 - 1)[B]_0/[A]_0 - r_1 + 1} \right\} \tag{7.7}$$

More complicated forms of this copolymer composition equation have been derived to cover the effect of penultimate[2] and prior[3] monomer units on the reactivity of the growing chain, and to cover the effect of depropagation reactions.[4,5]

Equation (3) can be used to present a graphical correlation of the polymer and monomer compositions, Fig. 7.1. Four specific relationships, which depend upon the relative magnitudes of the two reactivity ratios, become apparent.

In the first two cases the rate of disappearance of both monomers can become equal at a specific value of [A]/[B]. This value is known as

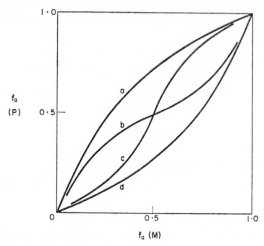

FIG. 7.1. Dependence of copolymer composition upon comonomer composition.

(a) $r_A > 1$, $r_B < 1$.
(b) $r_A = r_B < 1$.
(c) $r_A = r_B > 1$.
(d) $r_A < 1$, $r_B > 1$.

the "azeotropic composition", and can be found from equation (3) as

$$\frac{d[A]}{d[B]} = \frac{r_1[A] + [B]}{r_2[B] + [A]} = 1 \tag{7.8}$$

or

$$\left(\frac{[A]}{[B]}\right)_{AZ} = \frac{1 - r_2}{1 - r_1} \tag{7.9}$$

It is obvious from equation (9) that $([A]/[B])_{AZ}$ can have a finite positive value when $r_1, r_2 > 1$ or $r_1, r_2 < 1$. The monomer–polymer compositions for these cases are illustrated as curves b and c of Fig. 7.1. (No practical system has yet been discussed in free radical polymerization for which $r_1, r_2 > 1$.)

The two other cases occur when $r_1 > 1 \geqslant r_2$, and when $r_1 < 1 \leqslant r_2$. Under these conditions there is no azeotropic composition, and the polymer is always enriched (relative to the monomer feed) in the component of higher reactivity ratio. These conditions are shown as curves a and d of the figure.

A discussion of the computational procedures for obtaining r_1 and r_2 from experimental analyses of monomer and polymer compositions is set forth in the standard text by Alfrey, Bohrer and Mark.[6] It is convenient, however, to mention the graphical procedure most frequently used. In this method equation (3) is rearranged into a form such as

$$r_1 = \frac{\alpha - 1}{\beta} + \frac{\alpha}{\beta^2} \times r_2 \qquad (7.10)$$

where $\alpha = d[A]/d[B]$ and $\beta = [A]/[B]$ are the molar ratios of monomers A and B in the polymer and monomer feed respectively. For any pair of monomer and polymer compositions it is then possible to draw a straight line graph of r_1 against r_2. The intersection of a variety of such lines then yields r_1 and r_2 directly. Of course, due to experimental errors in the determination of α, a series of lines generally form a group of intersections enclosing a polygon, the centre of which is taken as the true point of intersection and the size of which is an estimate of random errors in the determination.

Monomer Sequence Lengths

Although equation (3) can be used to calculate the relative amounts of the two monomers in a binary copolymer, it gives no information on the way these monomers are distributed in the polymer chains. For example, a polymer containing 50 per cent of each monomer could exist as an alternating —ABAB— chain, as two distinct —AAA— and —B—B—B— blocks, or as any number of intermediate arrangements. The problem involved in discussing the frequency of any particular type of sequence in the chain is exactly the same as that encountered in studies of homopolymer stereoregularity.

The mean sequence lengths for each monomer type can be obtained from a study of the relative probabilities of each propagation reaction. Thus the probability that monomer A will add to a radical of type A is

$$P_{AA} = \frac{r_A[A]}{r_A[A] + [B]} = 1 - P_{AB} \qquad (7.11)$$

Similarly for formation of a —B—B· sequence

$$P_{BB} = \frac{r_B[B]}{r_B[B] + [A]} = 1 - P_{BA} \qquad (7.12)$$

The probability of formation of a sequence of m units of monomer A is then

$$P_A(m) = P_{AA}^{m-1} \times P_{AB} \qquad (7.13)$$

and for a sequence of m units of type B

$$P_B(m) = P_{BB}^{m-1} \times P_{BA} \qquad (7.14)$$

The mean sequence lengths are then

$$\left. \begin{aligned} \bar{m}_A &= \sum_{m-1}^{\infty} m P_A(m) \bigg/ \sum_{m-1}^{\infty} P_A(m) = (1 - P_{AA})^{-1} \\ \bar{m}_B &= \sum_{m=1}^{\infty} m P_B(m) \bigg/ \sum_{m=1}^{\infty} P_B(m) = (1 - P_{BB})^{-1} \end{aligned} \right\} \qquad (7.15)$$

Equations (13–16) are valid only for very long chains when the probability of forming a particular sequence is unaffected by the possible proximity of a chain end. Substitution in equations (11) and (12) yields

$$\bar{m}_A = \frac{r_A[A]}{[B]} + 1$$

$$\bar{m}_B = \frac{r_B[B]}{[A]} + 1 \qquad (7.16)$$

It is convenient at this juncture to introduce a run number, R, defined as the average number of monomer sequences occurring per 100 monomer units. As an example the copolymer section shown below contains twenty monomer units arranged in eleven runs or sequences (underlined), and has a run number of 55.

—A—B—B—A—A—A—B—A—B—B—B—B—A—A—B—A—B—B—A—A

The various copolymer properties which depend on the sequence distribution can then be described in terms of [A], [B], and R.

When the copolymer composition equation is derived in terms of the rate of sequence formation, ds/dt, we get

$$\frac{ds}{dt} = k_{AB}[A \cdot][B] + k_{BA}[B \cdot][A] \qquad (7.17)$$

$$\frac{d([A] + [B])}{dt} = k_{AA}[A \cdot][A] + k_{AB}[A \cdot][B]$$

$$+ k_{BA}[B \cdot][A] + k_{BB}[B \cdot][B] \ldots \qquad (7.1a)$$

Applying the stationary state approximation in the same way as before, combining equations (16), (17), we find

$$\frac{d([A] + [B])}{ds} = 1 + \frac{r_1}{2}\frac{[A]}{[B]} + \frac{r_2}{2}\frac{[B]}{[A]} \tag{7.18}$$

But, by definition $R = \dfrac{100 \, ds}{d([A] + [B])}$

so
$$R = \frac{200}{2 + r_1([A]/[B]) + r_2([B]/[A])} \tag{7.19}$$

Equation (19) allows us to use the monomer reactivity ratios to predict, not only the total amounts of A and B incorporated in the copolymer, but also their sequence arrangement.

Just as in the case of stereoregularity in homopolymers, a residual entropy is associated with the random arrangements of A and B sequences (of various lengths) in the copolymer. For the particular case when $P_{AA} = P_{BB} = P$, this entropy is $S_{AB}/k = -P \ln P - (1 - P) \ln (1 - P)$, where k is Boltzmann's constant.

More detailed discussions of the distribution of sequence lengths, the effect of finite molecular weight and of penultimate monomer units are available in the literature.[7-10]

Monomer and Radical Reactivity

On top of their obvious use in predicting the composition of a resulting copolymer, the monomer reactivity ratios can be used in a quantitative discussion of monomer and radical reactivity. Over the last two decades a great deal of work has been done on the classification of such reactivities, with the result that some extremely useful practical codifications have been obtained. The theoretical foundations of the reactivity variations, however, are not so clear.

The best known, and the most widely used, reactivity correlation is known as the Alfrey–Price Q–e scheme.[11] This scheme expresses each propagation rate constant in terms of four parameters representing the basic reactivities and polarities of the two species concerned. If the polarity of the radical and of the monomer are assumed to be the same,

$$\begin{aligned}
k_{pAA} &= P_A Q_A \exp(-e_A^2) \\
k_{pAB} &= P_A Q_B \exp(-e_A e_B) \\
k_{pBB} &= P_B Q_B \exp(-e_B^2) \\
k_{pBA} &= P_B Q_A \exp(-e_A e_B)
\end{aligned} \tag{7.20}$$

P and Q are proportional to the basic reactivities of the radical and monomer respectively, and e is proportional to the charge on the monomer unit.

Thus

$$r_A = \frac{Q_A}{Q_B} \exp\left[-e_A(e_A - e_B)\right] \tag{7.21}$$

$$r_B = \frac{Q_B}{Q_A} \exp\left[-e_B(e_B - e_A)\right] \tag{7.22}$$

$$r_A r_B = \exp\left[-(e_A - e_B)^2\right] \tag{7.23}$$

If the binary copolymerizations of n different monomers with one reference monomer of known Q,e have been investigated, the Q,e values of each of the n monomers can be calculated, thus allowing prediction of the $n(n-1)$ reactivity ratios for the other monomer combinations.

As can be seen, the usefulness of the classification depends on the assignment of Q and e values to a standard reference monomer. Styrene has been chosen for this purpose, and the scheme has been found to be self-consistent when $Q_{St} = 1 \cdot 0$, $e_{St} = -0 \cdot 8$.

TABLE 7.1

Some Q–e Values

Monomer	Q	e
Styrene	1	−0·8
Methyl methacrylate	0·74	+0·40
Vinyl acetate	0·02	−0·30
Acrylonitrile	0·44	+0·82
Vinyl chloride	0·03	+0·2
p-Bromo styrene	0·88	−0·2

The Q–e values for some well known monomers are listed in Table 7.1. From these values the reactivity ratios for any pair can be calculated using equations (21) and (22), and then the copolymer composition using equation (6).

The Q–e scheme is essentially a linear free energy relationship, in which some insight into the possible significance of Q and e is given by the equations

$$Q = \exp\left(-V/RT\right) \tag{7.24}$$

$$e = \varepsilon/(rDRT)^{1/2}$$

where r is the separation of radical and monomer in the transition state and D is the dielectric constant in the region between them. In this way it can be seen that q is an energy (about -2 to -3 kcal mole^{-1}) representing the relative resonance stabilization energy conferred on the radical being formed and ε (in e.s.u.) is the charge induced by the substituent on the carbon atom forming the new carbon–carbon bond in the transition state.

While a self-consistent comparison of reactivity ratios can be made using the Q–e scheme, and while the scheme correlates well with Hammet's σ–ρ functions, the temperature and dielectric constant dependence of Q–e does not seem to be fitted by equation (24). The scheme remains, then, an extremely useful comparative relationship, even although its exact theoretical significance is rather obscure.

The effects of polarity in copolymerization can also be discussed using the equation[12] introduced in Chapter 5 to cover transfer reactions

$$\log k_s = \log k_{3T} + \alpha\sigma + \beta$$

k_s is the rate constant for the addition reaction under study, k_{3T} is the rate constant for hydrogen abstraction from toluene and σ is Hammet's σ-value. Then α measures the intrinsic tendency of monomer (relative to toluene) to react by a polar mechanism: that is, the importance of charge transfer contributions to the transition state complex. Negative values of α correspond to electron-acceptor contributions, and positive values to electron donor.

For the case of homopolymerization a useful relationship is

$$\alpha = -5 \cdot 3\,\sigma$$

The $\alpha\beta$ scheme of Bamford and Jenkins can be best correlated with the Q–e scheme if $e = 0$ for styrene.

Rates of Copolymerization

The kinetic equations descriptive of copolymerization rates are derived in the same way as those relevant to ordinary homopolymerization. The stationary state concentration of free radicals is obtained by equating the rates of radical formation and termination, so that the final rate expression is dependent upon the mechanism of the termination process. For this reason it is necessary to discuss separately the two situations which exist when the rate of the termination process is controlled by either diffusive or chemical processes.

Let us turn first to the situation which exists when the termination rate is controlled by the chemical step in the overall process. Under these conditions the termination mechanism in a binary copolymerization is described by at least three different concurrent reactions. These reactions depend on the nature of the terminal monomer unit containing the electron of unpaired spin, and consist of two homo-termination and one cross-termination reaction

$$\sim A\cdot + \cdot A\sim \rightarrow \text{Polymer} \quad k_{tAA}$$
$$\sim B\cdot + \cdot B\sim \rightarrow \text{Polymer} \quad k_{tBB}$$
$$\sim A\cdot + \cdot B\sim \rightarrow \text{Polymer} \quad k_{tAB}$$

It is usual to apply the stationary state approximation in the form

$$\frac{d[A\cdot]}{dt} = \frac{d[B\cdot]}{dt} = 0 \qquad (7.25)$$

when $\qquad R_i = 2k_{tAA}[A\cdot]^2 + 2k_{tBB}[B\cdot]^2 + 2k_{tAB}[A\cdot][B\cdot] \qquad (7.26)$

and $\qquad k_{pAB}[A\cdot][B] = k_{pBA}[B\cdot][A] \qquad (7.27)$

The latter equation follows since one radical cannot increase in concentration at the expense of the other.

Substitution for $[A\cdot]$ from (27) into (26) yields the quadratic expression

$$\frac{R_i}{[B\cdot]^2} = \frac{2k_{tAA}k_{pBA}^2[A]^2}{k_{pAB}^2[B]^2} + 2k_{tBB} + \frac{2k_{tAB}k_{pBA}[A]}{k_{pAB}[B]} \qquad (7.28)$$

The overall rate of copolymerization is given by

$$-\frac{d([A]+[B])}{dt} = k_{pAA}[A\cdot][A] + 2k_{pAB}[A\cdot][B] + k_{pBB}[B\cdot][B] \qquad (7.29)$$

Substituting first for $[A\cdot]$ from (27) and then for $[B\cdot]$ from (26) yields

$$-\frac{d([A]+[B])}{dt}$$
$$= \frac{R_i^{1/2}(k_{pAA}k_{pBB}[A]^2 + 2k_{pAB}k_{pBA}[A][B] + k_{pBB}k_{pAB}[B]^2)}{(2k_{tAA}k_{pBA}^2[A]^2 + 2k_{tAB}k_{pBA}k_{pAB}[A][B] + 2k_{tBB}k_{pAB}^2[B]^2)^{1/2}} \qquad (7.30)$$

It is usual to simplify equation (30) by introducing the monomer reactivity ratios $r_A = k_{pAA}/k_{pAB}$, $r_B = k_{pBB}/k_{pBA}$, the substitutions $\delta_A = (2k_{tAA})^{1/2}/k_{pAA}$, $\delta_B = (2k_{tBB})^{1/2}/k_{pBB}$, and by assuming that the

7

cross-termination rate is the geometric mean of the two homo-terminations, when

$$\phi = \frac{k_{tAB}}{2(k_{tAA}k_{tBB})^{1/2}}$$

Then

$$-\frac{d([A]+[B])}{dt} = \frac{R_i^{1/2}(r_A[A]^2 + 2[A][B] + r_B[B]^2)}{(r_A^2\delta_A^2[A]^2 + 2\phi r_A r_B \delta_A \delta_B[A][B] + r_B^2\delta_B^2[B]^2)^{1/2}} \quad (7.31)$$

The rates of disappearance of the individual monomers are given by

$$-\frac{d[A]}{dt} = \frac{R_i^{1/2}(r_A[A]^2 + [A][B])}{D} \quad (7.32)$$

$$-\frac{d[B]}{dt} = \frac{R_i^{1/2}(r_B[B]^2 + [A][B])}{D} \quad (7.33)$$

where D is the denominator of equation (31).

Equation (31) is interesting since it predicts that when r_A and r_B are not too unequal, and when $\phi > 1$, the rate of copolymerization should pass through a minimum. Such minima, are, indeed often observed in practice. The situation is complicated, however, since the application of equation (31) to these cases yields values of ϕ which are either very large or composition dependent.

The ϕ-factor has been interpreted in terms of radical polarities similar to the $Q-e$ scheme. Under these circumstances ϕ should be similar to $(r_A r_B)^{-1/2}$, but the quantitative comparison of these quantities does not yield good agreement except when both are close to unity. On the other hand, it is a qualitative fact that ϕ is largest in those systems in which the propagation processes show a tendency towards alternation.

The case of a copolymerization in which one monomer does not undergo homopolymerization can be treated[15] in the same way as the normal binary copolymerization, when

$$\frac{-d([A]+[B])}{dt} = \frac{(r_A[A]^2 + 2[A][B])R_i^{1/2}}{\left(\frac{2k_{tAA}[A]^2}{k_{pAB}^2} + \frac{2k_{tAB}[A][B]}{k_{pAB}k_{pBA}} + \frac{2k_{tBB}[B]^2}{k_{pBA}^2}\right)^{1/2}} \quad (7.34)$$

If we now substitute $\delta_A = (2k_{tAA})^{1/2}/k_{pAA}$, $\zeta = (2k_{tBB})^{1/2}/k_{pBA}$, and $\phi = k_{tAB}/2(k_{tAA}k_{tBB})^{1/2}$, we find

$$-\frac{d([A]+[B])}{dt} = \frac{(r_A[A]^2 + 2[A][B])R_i^{1/2}}{(r_A^2\delta_A^2[A]^2 + 2\phi r_A \delta_A \zeta[A][B] + \zeta^2[B]^2)^{1/2}} \quad (7.35)$$

It is important to notice that this equation is not the same as would be obtained by simply setting $r_B = 0$ in equation (31). Differentiation of equation (35) shows[13] that, at constant total monomer concentration, the rate–composition curve can pass through a maximum provided that $r_A < 2$. While rate maxima have been observed in the copolymerization of methyl methacrylate and maleic anhydride, this particular system does not satisfy the condition $r_A < 2$, and it seems that this, and many other copolymerizations, are not correctly described in terms of three different termination processes.

A different kinetic description of the copolymerization rate must be made when the termination reaction is diffusion-controlled.[14] Under these circumstances the termination rate (and hence the denominator in our final rate expression) depends not upon the terminal monomer unit, but upon the composition of the whole chain. Since (at constant monomer composition) all terminating chains can be considered as having the same composition, there is only one diffusion-controlled termination rate constant, but this will vary with the composition of the monomer feed.

If the composition-dependent termination constant is designated $k_{t(AB)}$, the application of the stationary state approximation in the usual way gives

$$-\frac{(d[A] + [B])}{dt} = \frac{R_i^{1/2}(r_A[A]^2 + 2[A][B] + r_B[B]^2)}{(2k_{t(AB)})^{1/2}\left(\dfrac{r_A[A]}{k_{pAA}} + \dfrac{r_B[B]}{k_{pBB}}\right)} \qquad (7.36)$$

Equation (36) can be converted into a form similar to (31) by the substitutions $\varepsilon_A = (2k_{t(AB)})^{1/2}/k_{pAA}$, $\varepsilon_B = (2k_{t(AB)})^{1/2}/k_{pBB}$ where ε_A, ε_B are now composition-dependent variables.

$$-\frac{d([A] + [B])}{dt} = \frac{R_i^{1/2}(r_A[A]^2 + 2[A][B] + r_B[B]^2)}{(r_A^2\varepsilon_A^2[A]^2 + 2r_Ar_B\varepsilon_A\varepsilon_B[A][B] + r_B^2\varepsilon_B^2[B]^2)^{1/2}} \qquad (7.37)$$

In this equation there is no constant corresponding to ϕ, and the constants δ_A and δ_B of equation (31) have been replaced by composition-dependent variables. It must be stressed that a value of ϕ equal to unity need not necessarily be observed in a copolymerization with diffusion-controlled termination. The point is that the rates of the three chemical processes are not measurable by normal experimental procedures, and equation (31) is not applicable. If equation (31) should be used to calculate ϕ, then anomalous or composition-dependent values can very easily be obtained.

The copolymerization of vinyl acetate and methyl methacrylate has been shown[14] to involve a diffusion-controlled termination process, and in this system equation (36) gives a much more reasonable rate–composition relationship than equation (31). Indeed, at temperatures above 60°C the termination reaction can almost be described by the "ideal" equation

$$k_{t(AB)} = k_{tAA}x'_A + k_{tBB}x'_B \qquad (7.38)$$

where x'_A and x'_B are respectively the mole fraction of A-type and B-type monomer units in the polymer chain.

The rate of copolymerization when one monomer does not itself polymerize can be calculated in exactly the same way as before, and is

$$-\frac{d([A]+[B])}{dt} = \frac{R_i^{1/2}(r_A[A]^2 + 2[A][B])}{\varepsilon_A r_A[A] + \xi_B[B]} \qquad (7.39)$$

where $\varepsilon_A = (2k_{t(AB)})^{1/2}/k_{pAA}$, $\xi_B = (2k_{t(AB)})^{1/2}/k_{pBA}$ are composition-dependent variables replacing δ_A and ξ of equation (35).

The copolymerization of methyl methacrylate and maleic anhydride has been discussed in the light of equation (39). The termination reaction has been shown to be diffusion-controlled, and differentiation of equation (39) shows that a maximum in the rate–composition curve is possible without the restriction $r_A < 2$.

Although other copolymerizations have not yet been definitely shown to involve a diffusion-controlled termination process, very many (such as the copolymerizations of butyl acrylate with styrene or methyl methacrylate) seem better described by equations (37) and (39), than by equations (31) and (35).

In this section we have dealt solely with simple binary copolymerizations in which the rates of the various steps have been independent of the nature of the penultimate unit and of the radical chain length. The kinetic equations for three-monomer systems, or without these simplifying assumptions, are available in the literature.[3]

REFERENCES

1. MAYO, F. R. and LEWIS, F. M., *J. Amer. chem. Soc.*, 1944, **66**, 1594.
2. MERZ, E., ALFREY, T. and GOLDFINGER, G., *J. Polymer Sci.*, 1946, **1**, 75.
3. HAM, G. E., *Copolymerization*, Interscience (1964).
4. BARB, W. G., *Proc. roy. Soc.*, 1952, **A212**, 66, 177.
5. WALLING, C., *J. Polymer Sci.*, 1955, **16**, 315, (1955).
6. ALFREY, T., BOHRER, J. J. and MARK, H., *Copolymerization*, Interscience (1952).

7. STOCKMAYER, W. H., *J. chem. Phys.*, 1945, **13**, 199.
8. GOLDFINGER, G. and KANE, T., *J. Polymer Sci.*, 1948, **3**, 462.
9. MILLER, R. L. and NIELSON, L. E., *J. Polymer Sci.*, 1961, **46**, 303.
10. NORTH, A. M. and RICHARDSON, D., *Polymer*, 1964, **5**, 227.
11. ALFREY, T. and PRICE, C. C., *J. Polymer Sci.*, 1947, **2**, 101.
12. BAMFORD, C. H., JENKINS, A. D. and JOHNSTON, R., *Trans. Faraday Soc.*, 1959, **55**, 418.
13. BURNETT, G. M., *J. Polymer Sci.*, 1958, **28**, 642.
14. ATHERTON, J. N. and NORTH, A. M., *Trans. Faraday Soc.*, 1962, **58**, 2049.
15. POSTLETHWAITE, D. and NORTH, A. M., *Polymer*, 1964, **5**, 237.

CHAPTER 8

REVERSIBLE POLYMERIZATION

Introduction

Saturation of the double bond of an olefinic compound by groups which do not introduce steric strain into the resulting molecule is generally an exothermic process, and the addition of monomer units into a polymer chain is one such process. Depending on the molecular volume of groups substituted on the ethylenic double bond heats of polymerization may range from a maximum value of about 20 kcal mole^{-1}, to about 7 kcal mole^{-1}. The reaction whereby a monomer unit in a liquid becomes linked to a growing polymer chain, however, must involve a decrease in the entropy of the system. The change in the free energy of the system when a monomer unit is added to the polymeric chain is then given by

$$\Delta G = \Delta H - T \Delta S \qquad (8.1)$$

and will only be negative when ΔH is negative and $|\Delta H| > |T \Delta S|$.

For most of the common monomers which polymerize under normal conditions of temperature and pressure the free energy change is negative. However, there must be a temperature, perhaps not realizable in practical systems, when the free energy change is zero, or in fact positive. Above this temperature the addition of a monomer unit to a polymeric chain will involve an increase in the free energy of the system, whereas elimination of a monomer unit from the chain would lower the free energy. Consequently, in a system containing monomer and reactive polymer chains capable of either adding or eliminating monomer, the latter reaction will be more favoured. Since a polymeric chain with a free radical end is such an entity, there exists a temperature above which polymeric free radicals eliminate monomer rather than increasing in chain length, and consequently the production of high molecular weight polymer does not take place. This critical temperature is named the "ceiling temperature", and the reaction whereby monomer is eliminated, being the reverse of the propagation step, is called the "depropagation reaction".

Since the heat of polymerization decreases as the steric effects of groups substituted on the olefinic bond increases, a parallel decrease in the ceiling temperature is to be expected, and in fact certain monomers, such as α-methylstyrene, have a ceiling temperature which is in the neighbourhood of or below room temperature.

Introducing the depropagation reaction into the usual kinetic scheme of initiation, propagation, transfer and termination

$$R_n^{\cdot} + M \underset{k_d}{\overset{k_p}{\rightleftharpoons}} R_{n+1}^{\cdot}$$

for long chains the rate of polymerization is given by

$$R_p = (k_p[M] - k_d) R_i^{1/2}/(2k_t)^{1/2} \qquad (8.2)$$

and the degree of polymerization by

$$\bar{P}^{-1} = \frac{k_f[M]}{(k_p[M] - k_d)} + \frac{(2k_{t,d} + k_{t,c})R_p}{(k_p[M] - k_d)^2} \qquad (8.3)$$

The rate constants for the propagation and depropagation reactions can be expressed in an Arrhenius form,

$$k_p = A_p \exp(-E_p/RT) \text{ and } k_d = A_d \exp(-E_d/RT) \quad (8.4)$$

As for any reversible reaction, $E_p - E_d = \Delta H_p$. For long chains ΔH_p is equal to the heat of the overall polymerization. For those monomers which polymerize readily, ΔH_p is both negative and greater than E_p, so that E_d must be greater than E_p, and consequently the depropagation reaction can only become important compared with the propagation reaction at high temperatures. The ceiling temperature, when $k_p[M] = k_d$, can then be found directly as

$$T_c = \frac{\Delta H_p}{R \ln (A_p[M]/A_d)} \qquad (8.5)$$

If this value of the ceiling temperature is compared with the values obtained by setting the free energy change during propagation to zero,

$$T_c = \Delta H_p/\Delta S_p \qquad (8.6)$$

and

$$\Delta S_p = R \ln (A_p/A_d) + R \ln [M] \qquad (8.7)$$

Defining ΔS_p^0 as the entropy change for a monomer concentration of 1 mole l⁻¹,

$$T_c = \Delta H_p/(\Delta S_p^0 + R \ln [M]) \qquad (8.8)$$

Either equation (7) or equation (8) can be used to define an equilibrium concentration of monomer at a given temperature.

$$[\text{M}]_{\text{eq}} = \frac{A_d}{A_p} \exp\left(\frac{\Delta S_p}{R}\right) = \exp\left(\frac{\Delta S_p - \Delta S_p^0}{R}\right) \tag{8.9}$$

In practice equilibrium can only be achieved by continuous regeneration of free radicals, so that in normal solutions terminated polymer is usually stable at temperatures above the ceiling temperature.

Tabulated values of the entropies and enthalpies of polymerization of most common monomers are discussed in the review by Dainton and Ivin.[1]

Entropy of Stereoregularity

When a homopolymer can exist in stereoregular (isotactic or syndiotactic) and random (atactic) forms, it is obvious that stereospecificity must make a contribution to the total entropy of a polymer sample. By the same token, the entropy of polymerization of a monomer (capable of forming regular and random polymers) will depend on the stereoregularity of the final polymer.

The magnitude of this entropy, which has been called the entropy of stereoregularity, can be calculated from the number of possible arrangements of sequences of d-type and l-type asymmetric centres along a polymer molecule. Obviously, in both perfectly isotactic and perfectly syndiotactic polymer only one arrangement is possible, and the entropy is zero.

When P is the probability that any propagating asymmetric centre adds to monomer to form a centre of the same asymmetry, the entropy of stereoregularity is (for polymers of infinite molecular weight)

$$\Delta S_{\text{st}} = -P \ln(P) - (1 - P) \ln(1 - P)$$

This function is symmetrical about $P = 0.5$ which is the condition corresponding to completely random polymer. When the molecular weight is low, the maximum entropy is obtained when P is slightly less than 0.5.

It can be seen that absolutely random and perfectly stereospecific polymers differ in entropy by 1.4 cal deg^{-1}. If the ceiling temperature of a polymerization is normally close to room temperature, and if ΔH is about 8 kcal mole^{-1}, this entropy difference can cause a 15°C variation in the ceiling temperature for perfectly stereoregular and absolutely random polymerizations.

While this effect has not yet been reported in free radical polymerizations, it has been observed in the ionic polymerization of aldehydes.[6]

In exactly the same way the ceiling temperature of a copolymer will be greater than the value calculated from the ceiling temperatures of the components assuming that ΔH_p and ΔS_p vary linearly with composition.

Kinetics of Equilibrium Polymerization

Let us consider the general case where the initiation reaction as well as the propagation reactions may be reversible. The overall kinetic scheme is then, in absence of transfer

$$I + M \rightleftharpoons R_1^{\cdot} \qquad\qquad K_a$$

$$R_1^{\cdot} + M \rightleftharpoons R_2^{\cdot} \qquad\qquad K_b$$

$$\cdots\cdots\cdots\cdots\cdots\cdots\cdots\cdots\cdots$$

$$R_{n-1}^{\cdot} + M \rightleftharpoons R_n^{\cdot} \qquad\qquad K_n$$

$$\cdots\cdots\cdots\cdots\cdots\cdots\cdots\cdots\cdots$$

$$R_r^{\cdot} + R_s^{\cdot} \to \text{Inert Polymer} \quad \text{rate constant } k_t$$

where K_a, K_b, ... K_n ... are the equilibrium constants for the initiation and succeeding propagation reactions respectively. By analogy with the treatment of polymerization in the absence of depropagation, the assumption will be made that the constants K_b, K_c ... K_n, ... are all equal and can be represented by K_p. The kinetic problem to be solved is the relation between the equilibrium constants, K_a and K_p, and the equilibrium values of the degree of polymerization, the radical size distribution and the polymer size distribution. This generalized treatment can, of course, be applied to photo-initiated polymerization when monomer functions in place of the initiating species, I.

In the kinetic scheme set forth above an irreversible termination step has been included. It has been suggested by Tobolsky[2] that the degree of polymerization which is attained under equilibrium conditions is independent of the mechanism of the polymerization. This will be true even in the presence of an irreversible termination step, as is the case in most free radical polymerizations. In the treatment that follows it will be assumed that the propagation and depropagation reactions are sufficiently rapid by comparison with the initiation and termination reactions that the equilibrium concentrations of initiating species, I, and of free radicals of every chain length are attained.

The equilibrium concentration of free radicals containing n monomer units is defined by the equilibrium constants, K_a and K_p,

$$[R_n^\cdot] = K_p^{n-1} K_a [I]_E [M]_E^n \qquad (8.10)$$

The total concentration of free radicals is

$$[R\cdot]_T = \sum_{n=1}^{\infty} [R_n^\cdot] = K_a [I]_E [M]_E (1 - K_p [M]_E)^{-1} \qquad (8.11)$$

so that the mole fraction of all radicals which have a degree of polymerization, n, is

$$[R_n^\cdot]/[R\cdot]_T = (K_p [M]_E)^{n-1}/(1 - K_p [M]_E) \qquad (8.12)$$

Now for irreversible termination by combination,

$$\frac{d[A_n]}{dt} = \tfrac{1}{2} k_{tns} \sum_{s=1}^{s=n-1} [R_{n-s}^\cdot][R_s^\cdot] \qquad (8.13)$$

$$= \frac{\tfrac{1}{2} k_{tns}[R\cdot]_T^2}{(1 - K_p[M]_E)^2} (K_p[M]_E)^{n-2} (n-1) \qquad (8.14)$$

The total rate of polymer formation is, remembering that $k_{tns} = 2k_t$,

$$-\frac{d[A]_T}{dt} = \sum_{n=1}^{\infty} \frac{d[A_n]}{dt} = \frac{k_t [R\cdot]_T^2}{(1 - K_p[M]_E)^4} \qquad (8.15)$$

and the rate of monomer disappearance is

$$-\frac{d[M]_E}{dt} = \sum_{n=1}^{\infty} n \frac{d[A_n]}{dt} = \frac{2k_t[R\cdot]_T^2}{(1 - K_p[M]_E)^5} \qquad (8.16)$$

so that the number average degree of polymerization is

$$\bar{P} = -\frac{d[M]_E}{d[A]_T} = 2(1 - K_p[M]_E)^{-1} \qquad (8.17)$$

and the mole fraction of n-mer in inert polymer is

$$x_n = \frac{d[A_n]}{d[A]_T} = (n-1)(1 - K_p[M]_E)^2 (K_p[M]_E)^{n-2} \qquad (8.18)$$

It is important to stress that in this derivation the monomer concentration is the equilibrium value. The kinetic expressions derived are only strictly applicable to polymerizations carried out close to equilibria conditions, or in which inert polymer can be reactivated.

It is interesting to note that both the degree of polymerization and the polymer size distribution, being independent of the equilibrium concentration of initiator, the constant K_a, and the termination rate, are therefore independent of the rate of initiation in such a system. For termination by disproportionation,

$$\frac{d[A_n]}{dt} = k_{tns}[R_n^{\cdot}][R\cdot]_T \tag{8.19}$$

$$= k_{tns}[R\cdot]_T^2 (K_p[M]_E)^{n-1}/(1 - K_p[M]_E)$$

Again the total rate of polymer formation is

$$\frac{d[A]_T}{dt} = \sum_{n=1}^{\infty} \frac{d[A_n]}{dt} = \frac{2k_t[R\cdot]_T^2}{(1 - K_p[M]_E)^2} \tag{8.20}$$

and the rate of monomer disappearance is

$$\frac{-d[M]_E}{dt} = \sum_{n=1}^{\infty} \frac{n\,d[A_n]}{dt} = \frac{2k_t[R\cdot]_T^2}{(1 - K_p[M]_E)^3} \tag{8.21}$$

which leads to the number average degree of polymerization,

$$\bar{P} = \frac{-d[M]_E}{d[A]_T} = (1 - K_p[M]_E)^{-1} \tag{8.22}$$

and the mole fraction of n-mer in the inert polymer,

$$x_n = \frac{d[A_n]}{d[A]_T} = (K_p[M]_E)^{n-1}(1 - K_p[M]_E) \tag{8.23}$$

The value for the degree of polymerization, $(1 - K_p[M])^{-1}$, is the same as the value derived by Tobolsky for any system in which all steps are reversible.

When equilibrium concentrations of monomer, free radicals of all sizes, and initiating species (whether or not these be fragments of some unstable molecules) are attained in a polymerization system, the degree of polymerization and the polymer size distribution are dependent upon one equilibrium constant only, K_p, and are independent of the rate of initiation. This is in direct contrast to the conditions in an irreversible polymerization (or in a polymerization with some depropagation but in which equilibrium conditions are not attained) when both the degree of polymerization and the polymer size distribution depend upon the rate of initiation.

Polymer Degradation by Free Radical Mechanisms

It is obvious that if, in some way, free radicals may be produced on a polymer chain which is maintained at a temperature above the ceiling temperature, the polymer will be reduced to smaller fragments. Many polymers are stable at temperatures above the ceiling temperature only because of the difficulty of initiating degradative centres on the polymer molecule. The overall process whereby inert polymer is reduced to fragments of low molecular weight is referred to as degradation. It does not necessarily follow that all degradation reactions involve simple depropagation of a polymeric free radical, so that it is advantageous at this point to examine the various processes which may occur when a polymeric free radical is formed at temperatures sufficently high to lead to degradation.

Three general types of reaction are possible. The main chain may undergo successive chain scission reactions, the radical formed being stabilized by some transfer reaction other than the depropagation reaction, so that the overall process is one giving rise to fragments containing several monomer units (each fragment being of considerably shorter chain length than the original polymer). An alternative chain scission reaction is the continuous depropagation reaction leading to complete conversion of any polymeric free radical to monomer. The third degradation process does not involve fission of the main backbone chain of the polymer at all, but results in the elimination of some molecule from the side groups substituted onto the backbone chain of the polymer.

The course of radical-induced decomposition of a polymer may also be influenced by the manner in which the radicals are introduced onto the polymer chain. For example, the photo- or thermal decomposition of certain polymers follows a course which differs slightly from the oxidative degradation.

Degradation Involving Depropagation

A kinetic treatment of polymer degradation as a free radical chain reaction has been carried out by Simha, Wall and Blatz,[3] who proposed a reaction scheme involving initiation by fission of some covalent bond either at random in the polymer chain, or at the end of the chain, followed by depropagation and volatilization of the resulting monomer.

Initiation:
$$A_n \rightarrow R_j^{\cdot} + R_{n-j}^{\cdot}$$
$$A_n \rightarrow R_1^{\cdot} + R_{n-1}^{\cdot}$$

Depropagation: $\qquad$ $R_n^{\cdot} \rightarrow R_{n-1}^{\cdot} + M$

Transfer: $\qquad$ $R_n^{\cdot} \rightarrow A_j + R_{n-j}^{\cdot}$

$\qquad$ $R_n^{\cdot} + A_m \rightarrow A_n + A_{m-j} + R_j^{\cdot}$

Termination: $\qquad$ $R_n^{\cdot} + R_m^{\cdot} \rightarrow A_m + A_n$

The transfer reactions involve hydrogen atom abstraction by the free radical which may be intra- or intermolecular. The species formed by loss of the hydrogen atom is then postulated to decompose into a stable molecular species and another free radical by fission of a main-chain carbon–carbon bond in the vicinity of the locus of reaction.

The kinetic equations which have to be solved in connection with this scheme are rather complex; however, it is possible to apply a stationary state approximation to the concentration of free radicals in this system. When the kinetic chain length is considerably greater than the degree of polymerization of the initial polymer being degraded, which is assumed to be monodisperse in chain length, the number average degree of polymerization of the residue at any time is

$$\bar{P}_t = P_0 \frac{1 + \varepsilon\tau \dfrac{(N-1)(N+5)}{4(N-1)} - \varepsilon^2(\tau - \tau^2/_2)\dfrac{(N-7)(N-5)(N+3)}{24(N-1)}}{1 + \varepsilon\tau \dfrac{(N-5)}{2} - \varepsilon^2(\tau - \tau^2/_2)\dfrac{(N-5)(N-7)}{8}}$$

$$(8.24)$$

where $\varepsilon^{-1} = k_d/k_1^{1/2}k_t^{1/2}[A]^{1/2}$ is the kinetic chain length, P_0 is the chain length of the original polymer and $\tau = k_1 t$ where k_1 is the rate constant for the dissociative initiation step. N is the number of carbon atoms in the main chain of the original polymer, k_d and k_t being the rate constants for depropagation and termination respectively.

The fraction of polymer, which is of the original degree of polymerization, remaining at any time is given by

$$\frac{A_{N-1(\tau)}}{A_{N-1(0)}} = e^{3\tau - (N-1)\tau}$$

$$(8.25)$$

and the size distribution of the resulting polymer at any time is given by:

$$\frac{A_{J(\tau)}}{A_{N-1(0)}} = \varepsilon e^{3\tau} \left(2 - \frac{1}{N-J-1} \right) [e^{-J\tau} - e^{-(N-1)\tau}]$$

$$- \varepsilon^2 e^{3\tau} \left\{ \left[\frac{4e^{-2\tau}}{1 - e^{-2\tau}} - \frac{N-J-3}{2} \right] e^{-J\tau} \right.$$

$$\left. - \left[\frac{4}{1 - e^{-2\tau}} + \frac{3}{2}(N-J-3) \right] e^{-(N-1)\tau} \right\} \quad (8.26)$$

$$4 \leqslant J \leqslant N - 3$$

where J and N are respectively the number of carbon atoms in the main chains of the resulting heterodisperse and initial monodisperse polymer.

Degradation to Fragments of Random Size

When the rates of the transfer reactions are large compared with the rate of the depropagation reaction, the overall effect of the reaction is the same as a series of random fissions in the main chain of the original polymer. The resulting fragments range in size from monomer to polymer of chain length the same as that of the initial polymer. Simha and Wall[4] have shown that if k is the rate constant for the bond scission, the fraction of bonds broken is given by

$$\alpha = 1 - e^\tau \quad (8.27)$$

The number average chain length of the residue is

$$\bar{P}_{(\tau)} = \frac{J + \alpha(J - L)(L - 1)}{1 + \alpha(J - L)} \quad (8.28)$$

where L is the number of monomer units in the shortest chain which does not evaporate.

The conversion to volatile material is given by

$$C = 1 - (1 - \alpha)^{L-1} \left(1 + \frac{\alpha(J - L)(L - 1)}{J} \right) \quad (8.29)$$

and it is interesting to note that this expression predicts a maximum in the rate of formation of volatile molecules

$$\frac{dC}{d\tau} = (L-1)(1-C) - (1-\alpha)^L \frac{(J-L)(L-1)}{J} \quad (8.30)$$

occurring at

$$C_{max} = 1 - \left(\frac{L-1}{L}\right)^{L-1} \times \left(\frac{2L-1}{L}\right) \quad (8.31)$$

The statistics of random chain scission processes have been considered by Kuhn,[5] when ostensibly the same results are obtained.

Side Group Decomposition

In the degradation of certain polymers it is possible that some reaction other than depropagation is possible. Hydrogen abstraction reactions and transfer reactions have already been discussed. A further reaction is the elimination of the side group from the polymer chain. Although these eliminations need not necessarily proceed by a free radical mechanism, they are included here for the sake of completeness. Thus the degradation of poly-t-butyl methacrylate results in the formation of isobutene, leaving a residue which is a copolymer of methacrylic acid and methacrylic esters, which decompose into a polyene and the parent acid. In the same way, too, polyvinyl chloride loses hydrochloric acid to form a polymeric residue which is usually coloured due to the formation of conjugated lengths in the polymeric main chain.

Oxidative Degradation

The oxidation of polymers occurs by a free radical chain process, and can most conveniently be treated by considering separately unsaturated and saturated polymers.

Perhaps the most important unsaturated polymer is natural rubber, and certainly a great deal of time has been devoted to studying the oxidation of both natural and synthetic rubbers. In the preceding section on free radical degradation reactions, the treatment given contained the condition that the kinetic chain length was greater than the degree of polymerization of the initial polymer. If this condition is not necessarily fulfilled, the interesting situation arises whereby the initiation and transfer reactions lead to chain scission, and the termination reaction leads to the cross-linking of different chains. In fact, such a situation is characteristic of the oxidative degradation of unsaturated polymers.

When the oxidation is brought about by use of an initiator, the following simplified scheme can be used to represent the chain reaction,

Initiation: Initiator $\rightarrow$ 2R'$\cdot$ Rate R_i

R'$\cdot$ + RH $\rightarrow$ R'H + R$\cdot$ or R'RH$\cdot$

Propagation:

R$\cdot$ + O$_2$ $\rightarrow$ RO$_2\cdot$ Rate constant $k_{p,a}$

RO$_2\cdot$ + RH $\rightarrow$ RO$_2$H + R$\cdot$ $k_{p,b}$

Termination:

RO$_2\cdot$ + RO$_2\cdot$ $\rightarrow$ Inert products $k_{t,a}$

R$\cdot$ + R$\cdot$ $\rightarrow$ Inert products $k_{t,b}$

where RH represents a chain unit of the unsaturated polymer, which in the case of natural rubber would be a polyisoprene

$$(-CH_2-CH=C(CH_3)-CH_2)_n$$

The second stage of the initiation reaction is then either hydrogen abstraction from the polymer, or addition of the primary radical to one of the olefinic bonds of the polymer. Termination will be between two peroxy radicals only when the reaction is being carried out under high oxygen pressures when the concentration of ROO$\cdot \gg$ R$\cdot$. Under stationary state conditions the rate of reaction is

$$-\frac{d[O_2]}{dt} = \frac{k_{p,b}R_i^{1/2}[RH]}{(2k_{t,b})^{1/2}} \tag{8.32}$$

the corresponding equation for low oxygen pressure being

$$-\frac{d[O_2]}{dt} = \frac{k_{p,a}R_i^{1/2}[O_2]}{(2k_{t,s})^{1/2}} \tag{8.33}$$

In the absence of an initiator, oxygen can react directly with the double bond of the polymer to form a peroxy radical,

R—CH=CH—R' + O$_2$ $\rightarrow$ R—$\overset{\displaystyle\cdot}{C}$H—CH—R'
                                                                $\underset{\displaystyle\cdot}{\overset{|}{O}}O\cdot$

R—CH=CH—R' + R—CH—$\overset{\displaystyle\cdot}{C}$HR' $\rightarrow$ R—CH—$\overset{\displaystyle\cdot}{C}$H—R'
                         $\underset{\displaystyle\cdot}{\overset{|}{O}}O\cdot$ $\overset{|}{O}$
                                                                                                    $\overset{|}{O}$
                                                                                          R—$\overset{|}{C}$H—$\underset{\displaystyle\cdot}{C}$H—R'

The overall oxidation in either case is autocatalytic, since the peroxides or hydroperoxides which are formed can function as initiators. Incorporating the initiation reactions

$$\text{RH} + \text{O}_2 \rightarrow \cdot\text{RHOO}\cdot \qquad \text{Rate constant } k_{i,a}$$
$$\text{ROOH} \rightarrow \text{RO}\cdot + \cdot\text{OH} \qquad k_{i,b}$$
$$(2\text{R}\cdot)$$

into the reaction scheme in the absence of any other initiator, the overall rate of the reaction is given by

$$\frac{-\text{d}[\text{O}_2]}{\text{d}t} = \frac{k_{p,b}}{(2k_{t,b})^{1/2}}\,[\text{RH}]\,(k_{i,a}[\text{RH}][\text{O}_2] + 2k_{i,b}[\text{ROOH}])^{1/2} \qquad (8.34)$$

$$\frac{\text{d}[\text{ROOH}]}{\text{d}t} = \frac{k_{p,b}}{(2k_{t,b})^{1/2}}\,[\text{RH}](k_{i,a}[\text{RH}][\text{O}_2] + 2k_{i,b}[\text{ROOH}])^{1/2}$$
$$- k_{i,b}[\text{ROOH}] \qquad (8.35)$$

Under the conditions when a stationary state concentration of hydroperoxide exists,

$$[\text{ROOH}] = \frac{-\text{d}[\text{O}_2]}{\text{d}t}\Big/ k_{i,b} \qquad (8.36)$$

so that

$$\frac{-\text{d}[\text{O}_2]}{\text{d}t} = \frac{k_{p,b}}{(2k_{t,b})^{1/2}}\,[\text{RH}]\left(k_{i,a}[\text{RH}][\text{O}_2] + 2\,\frac{-\text{d}[\text{O}_2]}{\text{d}t}\right)^{1/2} \qquad (8.37)$$

It can be seen that cross-linking reactions result from any of the termination reactions, or from the initiation reaction involving direct attack of oxygen on the double bond of the unsaturated polymer unit. The origin of the chain scission reaction in the absence of the depropagation or transfer reactions discussed in the last section is rather more obscure. It was originally thought, by analogy with the behaviour of small molecules, that the chain scission occurred as a consequence of the decomposition of the hydroperoxide.

$$\begin{array}{ccccccc}
\text{OOH} & & \text{O}\cdot & & \cdot\text{OH} & \text{O} & \cdot\text{OH}\\
| & & | & & & \| & \\
\text{R}-\text{C}-\text{R}'' & \rightarrow & \text{R}-\text{C}-\text{R}'' & \rightarrow & & \text{R}-\text{C} + & \cdot\text{R}''\\
| & & | & & & | & \\
\text{R}' & & \text{R}' & & & \text{R}' &
\end{array}$$

More recently Tobolsky[2] has concluded that the scission reaction must occur in the termination reaction between two peroxy radicals.

Polymers which do not contain unsaturated groups are in general much more resistant to oxidation than those with unsaturated groups. Because of this, extensive oxidation can usually only be achieved at rather high temperatures when depropagation or other degradative reactions may become important. The principal features of the oxidation however, do seem to be the same as those observed in the oxidation of low molecular weight saturated compounds. The reaction is autocatalytic, and peroxides can be detected in amounts which are generally greater the lower is the reaction temperature. An interesting feature of the oxidation of polymeric species, and one illustrating the dangers of assuming that macromolecular compounds will undergo the same reactions as monomolecular prototypes, is found in a comparison of the autoxidations of cumene and polystyrene. In the former case cumene hydroperoxide is formed in almost quantitative yields, whereas the autoxidation of polystyrene occurs only with difficulty and is accompanied by decomposition of the polymer. The products obtained from this autoxidation have been used to support the formation of a hydroperoxide group on the tertiary carbon atom, but there is also considerable evidence for the formation of hydroperoxy groups attached directly to the benzene ring.

REFERENCES

1. DAINTON, F. S. and IVIN, K. J., *Quart. Rev. chem. Soc.*, 1958, **12**, 61.
2. TOBOLSKY, A. V., *Properties and Structure of Polymers*, Wiley (1960).
3. SIMHA, R., WALL, L. A., and BLATZ, P. J., *J. Polymer Sci.*, 1950, **5**, 615.
4. SIMHA, R. and WALL, L. A., *J. Polymer Sci.*, 1951, **6**, 39.
5. KUHN, W., *Ber. dtsch. chem. Ges.*, 1930, **63**, 1503.
6. NORTH, A. M. and RICHARDSON, D., *Polymer*, 1964, **5**, 227.

CHAPTER 9

SOLID STATE POLYMERIZATION

DESPITE the considerable amount of work being done in this sphere, the processes involved and their role in the overall reaction are still rather obscure. As a consequence of this any discussion of the problem is qualitative rather than quantitative. The phenomena observed and the hypotheses advanced are so fascinating, however, that they deserve further description at this point.

Several problems have to be faced in interpreting solid state free radical reactions. The position and extent of inter-crystallite boundaries and of dislocations must be clearly known before any interpretations can be made as to the exact locus of the reaction. Furthermore, the nature of the monomer order and geometry in the crystal must also be known. Finally, the uniform generation of free radicals in the crystal is a necessary prerequisite for a "homogeneous" reaction. This last requirement usually requires an irradiation technique, and there is then no guarantee (particularly for high energy irradiation) that the monomer molecules in the track of the incident quantum (or of any recoil particles) exist in the same ordered low temperature configuration as in the remainder of the crystal.

Two facts are immediately apparent. With one or two interesting exceptions, the Van der Waals separation of monomer molecules is greater than the polymer covalent bond length, so that some mechanism for contraction is required before propagation can proceed. Secondly, free radical termination processes will occur only if the centres of radical activity (or some terminating agent) are capable of long-range movement.

The Site of the Polymerization Reaction

Experiments designed to discover the locus of the polymerization reaction all indicate that some sort of disorder is a necessary prerequisite for the growth reaction.

The detailed studies of Bamford, Eastmond and Ward[1] on the photopolymerization of acrylic acid and methacrylic acid indicate that the polymerization occurs at crystal dislocations. Since these are normally distributed throughout the crystal in a random fashion, the reaction appears to be proceeding homogeneously throughout the crystal.

Of course the formation of polymer can automatically create a phase boundary, and it has been suggested[2,3] that the reaction occurs at these boundaries so as to minimize the strain energy at the interface. Optical studies of the resulting polymer–monomer mixture certainly seem to confirm this interpretation. The general conclusion is that polymerization can occur within the actual crystal only when there exists some associated mobility such as is found in the pre-melting temperature region or at temperatures which correspond to some phase change.

Whatever the exact locus of the reaction, the process depends on the actual crystal structure of the monomer. This has been shown by examination of two polymorphic forms of the same monomer, and the studies of Chen and Grabar[4] on vinyltributylphosphonium bromide have been particularly illuminating. In this case the two polymorphic forms exhibit the same overall Arrhenius activation energies, but different pre-exponential factors. The rate is highest in the metastable isomorph.

One of the most interesting aspects of solid state polymerizations is the fact that they can occur with great rapidity during phase changes in the solid monomer. These phase changes may be glass–crystal transitions, or transitions from one isomorphic form to another. That long-range diffusion of reactants can take place during these phase changes is markedly demonstrated by the fact that even radical–radical termination reactions take place under these conditions.

Detailed studies of radical termination reactions in solid monomer have been carried out on acrylonitrile.[5,6] This monomer can exist in two possible solid forms with a first order transition temperature between them at $-113 \cdot 5°C$. A second order transition temperature (considered as a glass transition by the Russian workers) exists at about $-165°C$, below which the high temperature form cannot spontaneously revert to the low temperature isomorph. The monomer melting point is $-83°C$. When the monomer is rapidly cooled to $-196°C$, the solid consists of a non-equilibrium mixture of both phases. If free radicals are formed in the solid and the whole allowed to warm, radical recombination reactions can be observed from temperatures of $0 \cdot 8$–$0 \cdot 9$ T_p up to T_p, where T_p represents the temperature of any one of the three phase transitions mentioned above. The propagation reaction also proceeds in these temperature zones.

The importance of phase transitions in the propagation reaction is shown by the fact that a frozen mixture containing monomer and a high concentration of active species (radicals or ions) can explode on being warmed to a transition temperature.

The Influence of the Lattice on the Propagation Rate

We have already seen that polymerization can proceed at different rates in the two polymorphic forms of vinyltributylphosphonium bromide, but the exact mechanism for an enhanced Arrhenius pre-exponential factor in the metastable form remains obscure. The problem, indeed, can be stated quite generally as to whether the crystalline lattice is an aid or a hindrance to the polymerization process.

At present the question is not resolved, and it is only possible to summarize the main arguments and observations for both views.

An interesting suggestion in favour of a benign lattice effect has been put forward by Semenov.[7] Basically the suggestion is that some electronic interaction occurs between the ordered monomer molecules which can be considered as existing in partial conjugation. The addition of a radical to the first monomer molecule in such a region then brings about the almost simultaneous addition of all the molecules in the "conjugated" domain. The locus of radical activity thus moves through the region of interacting monomer molecules with the velocity of an electron wave. There is not yet any decisive evidence for the verification of this combined radical chain and energy chain process, since all examples quoted are also capable of alternative explanations.

It has also been suggested[8] that the lattice exerts a benign influence on polymerizations with a low heat of polymerization and consequently a low ceiling temperature. The argument is that the entropy of polymerization, crystalline monomer to polymer, is less negative (and may even be positive) than the entropy of polymerization, liquid monomer to polymer. Thus the monomer melting point may be above the ceiling temperature for the latter reaction, but below the ceiling temperature for the crystal monomer reaction. Under these conditions polymerization should be possible at the liquid–crystal interface.

This hypothesis has been questioned by Heikens and Geelen,[9] who point out that at equilibrium the lower entropy of the crystal monomer is balanced by its lower enthalpy, and the free energy of polymerization should be the same from both phases!

The final argument in favour of a benevolent lattice effect suggests that if the monomer molecules should be favourably oriented, the steric factor in a collision theory of reaction rates should be larger than in liquids. Such a favourable lattice configuration does seem to exist for p-acetamido- and p-benzamidostyrene.[10] Several examples of an unfavourable lattice effect can be quoted. Thus laurylammonium acrylate polymerizes more slowly in the liquid crystal than in dilute solution, and irradiated methyl methacrylate at low temperatures polymerizes as a supercooled glass but not as a crystalline solid.

In general, it seems that the main criterion for polymerization is one of mobility, and the fact that many "solid" monomers polymerize predominantly in the premelting zone suggests that lattice defects (rather than lattice perfection) are required.

REFERENCES

1. BAMFORD, C. H., EASTMOND, G. C. and WARD, J. C., *Proc. roy. Soc.*, 1963, **A271**, 357.
2. ADLER, G., BALLANTINE, D. and BAYSAL, B., *J. Polymer Sci.*, 1960, **48**, 195.
3. BAYSAL, B., ADLER, G., BALLANTINE, D. and COLOMBO, P., *J. Polymer Sci.*, 1960, **44**, 117.
4. CHEN, C. S. H. and GRABAR, D. G., Int. Symp. Macromolecules, Paris (1963).
5. KARGIN, V. A., KABANOV, K. A. and PAPISSOV, I. M., *ibid.*
6. BENSASSON, R., DWORKIN, A. and MARX, R., *ibid.*
7. SEMENOV, N. N., *J. Polymer Sci.*, 1961, **55**, 563.
8. KARGIN, K. A., KABANOV, K. A. and ZUBOV, V. P., *Doklady A.N. U.S.S.R.*, 1960, **134**, 1098.
9. HEIKENS, D. and GEELEN, H., *Polymer*, 1962, **3**, 591.
10. JAKABHAZY, S. Z., MORAWETZ, H. and MOROSOFF, N., Int. Symp. Macromolecules, Paris (1963).

CHAPTER 10

HETEROGENEOUS POLYMERIZATIONS

HETEROGENEOUS polymerizations may be divided into two main classes. The first type are reactions which are initially homogeneous but in which the polymer forms a second phase as the reaction proceeds. This class of reaction can be observed in the bulk polymerization of acrylonitrile and vinylidene chloride, in certain butadiene polymerizations, in "gas-phase" polymerizations, and in certain high pressure ethylene polymerizations. A convenient generic name for such reactions is "precipitation polymerization". The second major class of heterogeneous reactions involves an initial two phase system, usually with monomer present as a dispersed phase. The well-known and technically important emulsion and suspension polymerizations come into this class.

Precipitation Polymerization

The unusual kinetic features of these polymerizations can be described in terms of the diffusion-controlled reactions of polymeric radicals occluded in the highly viscous polymer.

When the polymer phase is swollen with monomer or solvent, diffusion of monomer is possible, but diffusion of the macroradicals is very considerably retarded. The net result is that the growth reaction continues almost unhindered, but the termination process is markedly reduced. The overall effect is an increase in the radical concentration and hence in the rate of polymerization as more and more radicals become incorporated (and physically "stabilized") in the viscous phase. If the polymer–monomer miscibility is very low, or if the polymerization is carried to very high conversion, the precipitated polymer is a solid rather than a swollen gel, and even the propagation reaction becomes impossible. The kinetic result is the same as if the trapped free radicals are being removed from the system, and the reaction can be described as a first order termination process. Of course these trapped radicals can be detected by electron spin resonance spectroscopy, and can react further if the polymer can be dissolved in, or made permeable to, another reactive substrate, or if the polymer is heated above its softening point.

The complete range of possibilities is illustrated by the polymerization of acrylonitrile in the presence of added quantities of N,N-dimethylformamide.[1] In the bulk polymerization with no additive the polymer is formed as a solid precipitate in which neither propagation nor termination can easily occur. When a small percentage of diluent is present, the polymer separates as a swollen gel in which propagation, but not termination can occur. The net result is a rate of polymerization greater than that of undiluted monomer. When more than 50 moles percent diluent are present the polymer phase becomes soluble, both propagation and termination can occur, and the rate is markedly reduced. Similar behaviour is observed when the temperature, rather than the concentration of diluent, is raised.

The kinetics of the polymerization when the occluded radicals may propagate (in swollen precipitates) have been discussed by Bamford and Jenkins.[2]

The principal difficulties in any discussion lie in the prediction of reasonable values for the rate of occlusion of free radicals and of the variation in the reaction rate constants as the extent of occlusion alters.

Bamford and Jenkins have used measurements of the total concentration of radicals, $[R]_t$, after a time of photopolymerization, t_p, to estimate the fraction of total radicals produced which become trapped. The mean rate of polymerization over a given conversion, ΔM, is given by

$$R_p = kR_i^\alpha \tag{10.1}$$

where k is a composite constant (at any given conversion), R_i is the rate of initiation and $1 \geqslant \alpha \geqslant 0.5$ depending on the relative importance of first order radical stabilization and second order termination. Then

$$t_p = \frac{\Delta M}{kR_i^\alpha} \tag{10.2}$$

over a small conversion increment.

The concentration of free radicals able to propagate is given by

$$[R\,\cdot] = kR_i^\alpha/k_p M \tag{10.3}$$

The rate of radical trapping is

$$R_{tr} = [T]/t_p \tag{10.4}$$

where $[T]$ is the total concentration of trapped radicals after time t_p.

Then

$$R_t/[\text{R} \cdot] = k_p[\text{M}][\text{T}]/\Delta M \qquad (10.5)$$

where $R_t/[\text{R} \cdot]$ is the mean probability that a given radical will become trapped in unit time. Then the fraction of all radicals which becomes trapped is

$$f_t = [\text{T}]/R_i t_p = k^{1/\alpha} R_p^{1-(1/\alpha)}[\text{T}]/\Delta M \qquad (10.6)$$

f_t is only slightly dependent on the rate of reaction, and is about 1 per cent in the bulk polymerization of acrylonitrile at room temperatures.

The kinetics of precipitation polymerization have been further examined by Durup and Magat.[3] These authors postulate a kinetic scheme in which termination is almost entirely due to small, or primary, radicals. Under these conditions a stationary state concentration of small radicals exists, but the large trapped propagating radicals never reach a stationary state concentration. Since Durup and Magat use a single propagation rate constant, the scheme can only be applicable to systems where polymer precipitates out in a swollen gel, and propagation is relatively unhindered.

Writing the kinetic scheme as

$$\text{Initiator} \to 2\text{R} \cdot \qquad \text{Rate } R_i$$
$$\text{R} \cdot + \text{M} \to \text{R}_1 \cdot \qquad \text{Rate } k_i[\text{R} \cdot][\text{M}]$$
$$\text{R}_n \cdot + \text{M} \to \text{R}_{n+1}^{\cdot} \qquad \text{Rate } k_p[\text{R}_n \cdot][\text{M}]$$
$$\text{R}_n \cdot + \text{R} \to P \qquad \text{Rate } k_t[\text{R}_n \cdot][\text{R} \cdot]$$

where $[\text{R} \cdot]$ and $[\text{R}_n \cdot]$ are primary radicals and propagating radicals respectively, the differential equation may be integrated to

$$\tau = - Z - \ln |1 - 2Z| \qquad (10.7)$$

where

$$\tau = \frac{R_i k_t}{2k_i[\text{M}]} t$$

and

$$Z = \frac{k_t}{2k_i[\text{M}]} [\text{R}_n \cdot]$$

The relative conversion is given by

$$\frac{\Delta M}{M} = \frac{4k_i^2 k_p[\text{M}]^2}{k_t^2 R_i} \int_0^\tau Z \, d\tau \qquad (10.8)$$

The quantity $\int_0^\tau Z \, d\tau$ can be approximated by a straight line in the region $\tau = 0{\cdot}1$ to $1{\cdot}0$, when

$$\frac{\Delta M}{M} \sim C^{te}(R_i)^{0{\cdot}8} \qquad (10.9)$$

where C is a constant.

Suspension Polymerization

A polymerization in which very fine monomer droplets, containing dissolved initiator, are suspended in a non-solvent (usually water) is known as a suspension polymerization. Although the suspension may be stabilized by solid or colloidal materials, these additives play no part in the polymerization process. Each monomer droplet functions as an individual reaction vessel. If radicals can be terminated singly, or if the efficiency of initiation is not unity the conventional kinetic behaviour is exhibited. Indeed the dispersing phase serves only to maintain a convenient viscosity for the complete system, and efficiently dissipates the heat of reaction.

Under ideal conditions when the radicals are formed and terminate in pairs, the particles contain only even numbers of radicals, and the conventional rate equation is modified to

$$R_p = \frac{k_p}{(2k_t)^{1/2}} \times R_i^{1/2} \tanh (N^2 v^2 R_i / 2 k_t)^{1/2} \qquad (10.10)$$

where v is the volume of the droplets, and N is Avogadro's number.

Emulsion Polymerization

When the monomer is dispersed as a stable emulsion in a non-solvent, but when the initiator is soluble only (or principally) in the dispersing medium, the system is known as an emulsion polymerization. In such reactions the fact that the initiator and monomer exist in different phases is all important, and consequently the emulsifying agents play a large part in controlling the kinetics of the reaction.

The important kinetic features exhibited by an emulsion polymerization are currently treated using an approach suggested by Smith and Ewart.[4] The basic mechanism of the polymerization is described by the following sequence of events.

(a) A free radical is formed in the dispersing medium, diffuses to a monomer droplet, is absorbed through the surfactant and initiates polymerization.

(b) The growing radical has a very low diffusivity and solubility in the dispersing medium, and thus continues to propagate (perhaps undergoing transfer reactions) until another radical enters the same droplet and mutual termination becomes possible.

(c) The original droplet becomes converted to a swollen monomer–polymer particle, and the supply of monomer to this droplet is maintained by diffusion from pure monomer droplets.

(d) After a certain time the number of particles (which now contain monomer and polymer) becomes stationary, and polymerization in any particle is alternately initiated and terminated by entry of single radicals.

The most important aspect of this mechanism is that any particle contains only one radical for only half the elapsed time so long as the rate of diffusion of radicals to the particles is constant. Under these conditions the rate of polymerization is independent of the rate of initiation, and is given by

$$-\frac{d[M]}{dt} = \tfrac{1}{2}k_p[M]_d \frac{N}{\mathbf{N}} \tag{10.11}$$

where $[M]_d$ is the concentration of monomer in the monomer–polymer droplet, N is the number of such droplets per litre of emulsion and $\mathbf{N}$ is Avogadro's number.

The mean lifetime of each radical is the time between successive entries of single radicals into a particle and is

$$\tau = \frac{N}{R_i \times \mathbf{N}} \tag{10.12}$$

This equation assumes that all radicals formed in the aqueous phase, at a rate R_i moles l^{-1} s^{-1}, diffuse to an emulsified particle before undergoing a termination reaction. Such an assumption has been verified experimentally.

Since both the rate of polymerization and the radical lifetime depend upon the number of particles in the system, calculation of this quantity forms an important part of the Smith–Ewart theory.

The calculation is based upon an examination of the rate of diffusion of free radicals into micellar soap, the surface area of which decreases with time as more and more soap becomes involved in the stabilization of monomer–polymer growing particles.

In order to simplify the calculation it is necessary to make several assumptions. In the first place it will be assumed that the rate of formation of new particles is negligible once all the soap has been converted from the micellar to the adsorbed form. A further apparently justifiable approximation is that the interfacial area per gramme of the soap is the same in the micelles and in the adsorbed state. Finally, it is necessary to simplify the function descriptive of the competition between particles and micelles for free radicals.

A "zero-order" approximation can be made by assuming that all the free radicals formed enter micelles (none entering ready formed particles). In this case the number of particles is simply equal to the number of radicals formed in the time elapsing between the start of the reaction and the moment when all the micellar soap is converted to adsorbed soap. Then the quantity to be determined is the time, t'', at which the total particle surface area becomes equal to the total interfacial area of the soap.

The number of particles is $N = R_i t''$ where R_i is the rate of formation of free radicals.

Let $\mathrm{d}V/\mathrm{d}t$ be the rate of growth of a particle and let it be constant over the time under discussion. Then the surface area, at time t, of a spherical particle which started growth at time t' is

$$A_t = (4\pi)^{1/3} \left\{ 3 \frac{\mathrm{d}V}{\mathrm{d}t} (t - t') \right\}^{2/3} \tag{10.13}$$

The total particle surface area is obtained by integrating from time zero to time t'' when

$$A_p = (4\pi)^{1/3} \left(3 \frac{\mathrm{d}V}{\mathrm{d}t} \right)^{2/3} R_i \int_0^{t''} (t - t')^{2/3} \, \mathrm{d}t' \tag{10.14}$$

$$= 0\cdot6(4\pi)^{1/3} \left(3 \frac{\mathrm{d}V}{\mathrm{d}t} \right)^{2/3} R_i (t'')^{5/3} \tag{10.15}$$

Then

$$N = R_i t'' = 0\cdot53 \left(R_i \Big/ \frac{dV}{dt} \right)^{2/5} (a_s S)^{3/5} \tag{10.16}$$

where a_s is the surface area per unit weight of the soap, present as a total weight S.

Since this treatment neglects those radicals which enter ready formed particles and are lost to the system, it must over-estimate the number of particles formed.

A similar (but more complex) calculation can be carried out for the "first-order" approximation that particles do trap radicals, and that the trapping efficiency is the same (per unit area of soap) on both the particle and the micelle. This treatment yields

$$N = 0{\cdot}37 \left(R_i \middle/ \frac{\mathrm{d}V}{\mathrm{d}t} \right)^{2/5} (a_s S)^{3/5} \tag{10.17}$$

This calculation differs from equation (16) only in the value of the numerical factor. The true situation must lie between these two limiting cases. However, the fractional power dependence of the number of particles on the weight of soap and on the rate of initiation is observed in practice.

REFERENCES

1. BAMFORD, C. H., JENKINS, A. D. and JOHNSTON, R., *Proc. roy. Soc.*, 1957, **A241**, 354.
2. BAMFORD, C. H. and JENKINS, A. D., *Proc. roy. Soc.*, 1955, **A228**, 220.
3. DURUP, M. and MAGAT, M., *J. Polymer Sci.*, 1955, **18**, 586.
4. SMITH, W. V. and EWART, R. H., *J. chem. Phys.*, 1948, **16**, 592.

INDEX